peace
for life

Freedom from problems for good

SANDY NEWBIGGING

Antony Rowe Publishing

A record for this title is available from the British Library.

Disclaimer: The medical information and all procedures mentioned and contained in this book are not intended to be used or construed as a substitute for professional medical care and advice provided by a physician. People who read this book and make decisions regarding their health or medical care which they believe are based on ideas contained in this book do so at their *own risk*. The author or publishers are making no medical claims. The author and publishers are not responsible for any adverse effects or consequences resulting from the use of any of the suggestions or information contained in this book, but offer this material as information which the public has a right to hear and utilize at its own discretion.

Privacy protection: Case study 'success stories' have been gathered from the author's consultation notes between 2005-2010 and the case notes of independent Mind Detox Method (MDM) Practitioners. Client names have been changed to respect privacy. All case studies from independent MDM Practitioners have been used with gratitude and on faith that they accurately reported the outcomes. Wordings of comments have been edited slightly for readability purposes only.

ISBN 978-1-907571-10-7

Printed and bound in Great Britain by
CPI Antony Rowe, Chippenham and Eastbourne

*To my Teacher, without you this book
would be missing Part 3.*

'Life is meant to be lived in eternal joy, infinite freedom, unconditional love and unbounded awareness. Any other life is utterly missing the point of being born a human.'

MSI

CONTENTS
Look within to find peace

PEACE FOR LIFE

FOREWORD
One truth
By Barefoot Doctor

The truth is the truth - there's only one and it's ineffable. The ways of describing it are myriad, though all have one thing in common: the power of metaphor. Metaphor is how we point to the way. When someone's metaphor resonates with you, even or especially if it's different from your own, it helps not only stretch your mind but also reinforce your own way by reminding you of what you already know, but might have forgotten in the rush.

When I met Sandy, I was instantly struck by his enthusiastic approach to spreading his word, and his courage in dedicating himself to forging a fresh path.

I recognized myself in him, and was deeply touched by the quality of his soul.

In this magnificent new book of his, through his innovative metaphor, alluding to the same truth and path I point to myself in all my work, he does so in a totally unique, original way. So that though I've written 14 books on the same topic, which normally leaves me nonplussed by offerings of a similar vein, I have been highly inspired reading this one and feel privileged to be writing the foreword.

As he so eruditely observes, inner peace and the joy deriving thereof, is not brought about so much by changing your thinking as some would have us believe, but by shifting the whole process of thinking itself, namely by entering the meditation state, whence pure awareness arises.

Pure awareness, uncluttered by thoughts of how well or badly you're doing in the game of local life, untroubled by the usual internal commentary and debate, facilitates the emptiness, hence receptivity espoused in the Taoist tradition I live by and teach myself. Being empty and in a peaceful state, they say, even gods and spirits are drawn to you bearing great gifts, let alone mere mortals.

In other words, seek peace and all else will be added.

In PEACE FOR LIFE, Sandy shows you how in the most splendidly eloquent way and I've no doubt you'll enjoy and benefit from each and every word.

Barefoot Doctor
Best-selling author

THANK YOU
For keeping the truth alive

First, I'd like to thank Lindsey Dayavati Best for your love, support and silliness. Thanks to my family for your unending belief and encouragement. Special thanks, as always, goes to Bryce Redford, for being a light-hearted rock in my life. And also to Narain, words cannot express the love, respect and gratitude I have for you. I would also like to thank the Ishayas' for keeping the truth alive and for keeping the path pure and playful.

Thanks to Barefoot Doctor for writing a great foreword. Thanks to David Hamilton - our chat on the train to Land's End got me going with this book. Thanks to Richard Price for proofreading the book, to Jenny Brown and Sharon O'Connell for your advice, and to Andrew and Esther Pepper for your encouragement and support. Thanks to the Mind Detox Practitioners around the world for your desire to make a positive difference. I am grateful to every person who has attended my talks, clinics, workshops and retreats. Without your courage to step beyond your challenges this book would not have been possible.

Finally, infinite gratitude goes to my Teacher, MKI. Thank you for reminding me how to play and for showing me that peace for life is only the beginning.

INTRODUCTION
Miracle or method?

A few years ago I was invited to work as a therapist on a detox health retreat in Southern Spain. With no idea of what to expect (at that time I thought detox was only for drug addicts!), I packed my bag and headed off for a week in the sun. It rained, heavily, the entire time! I'm not sure if it was the lack-of-sun that week or what, but my therapy schedule quickly became fully booked.

In more ways than just the location, I found myself in unfamiliar territory. Many of the detoxers were investing in their health because they were suffering from physical problems. That week I was to meet people suffering with migraines, irritable bowel syndrome (IBS), infertility, bulimia, obesity and psoriasis. This meant that not only was I suddenly working in the field of 'health', but due to my schedule, only had a couple hours with each of them.

A fortunate coincidence

Two weeks prior to going to Spain I had been invited to a talk by a specialist in the mind-body connection called Dr David Hamilton. During that inspiring talk (come to think of it, on another very wet day, this time just outside Glasgow), he shared many scientific studies that have investigated the power of the mind, including the mind's ability to heal the body.

With his message springing to the forefront of my own mind that day in Spain, I knew I had to update my therapeutic approach, fast. I suggested to my first client that we explore whether there might be any mental or emotional issues from their past that could be causing their physical problems today. With their agreement we proceeded.

Hmmm, to my next question...

I had no idea what to ask! I remember looking down at my blank notebook and then up again to meet the expectant eyes of my client. I decided to keep it simple by asking if there was an event in her life that might be causing her health condition, such that if we were to resolve it, the body would heal.

To both of our amazements, she immediately had an answer; a specific event had just 'popped into her mind'. With only a few more questions, we could see a possible link between the past emotional event and the current physical condition. Once we had established the possible cause, we worked on releasing any negative emotions associated with it and the session was done.

The healing power of peace

Time after time, in session after session, this happened with great success. Over the coming months I regularly witnessed **instantaneous remissions** from health conditions; I saw skin conditions clear up, chronic pain vanish, and digestion problems disappear to name but a few. Along with the healing of many other emotional issues and life problems too – all from helping people to get peace with their past.

Lucky break

News about my method, which by this point was becoming known as 'Mind Detox', then spread internationally when I was shown on three separate television series documenting people going through a mind-body detox retreat. The TV exposure and subsequent book deals lead to the opportunity of working with hundreds of people at my clinics, workshops and retreats around the world.

It's a miracle! (Or is it?)
Over time I became curious. Was I bearing witness to miracles? Was I some kind of gifted healer? Or had I simply stumbled across a method of healing that could be transferable and used by others?

For the next year I started using the same therapeutic questions when working with clients at my clinics and retreats. Very quickly it became clear that the power of the method was the method itself, and the possibility of training others was real. Soon after I ran my first Mind Detox Masterclass and Practitioner Certification Course and started training people from around the world via my Academy.

Reality check
Everything was going great. I was achieving all my goals, and was living what I thought was a successful life. But then, out of the blue reality hit me. Despite my life being exactly how I'd always wanted it to be, I realised I wasn't happy yet, nor was I experiencing much peace either.

I was shocked to realise that irrespective of all the work I'd done to change my mind, I was still experiencing negative thoughts and emotions on a regular basis. What made matters worse was noticing it was the same experience for my clients. Although we'd healed a physical condition or improved their life, they weren't necessarily experiencing true peace of mind yet either.

My rock bottom wake up call

Feeling hopeless, not to mention a complete fraud, I realised I could no longer rely on my future to fulfil me. I knew continuing to work so hard to accomplish bigger and better goals wasn't going to relieve my eternal itch that *there must be more to life than this*.

To make matters worse, my increasing frustration led to a rocky time in my relationship, which inevitably ended with my partner leaving. Along with the beautiful child I'd been raising, the great house I was living in, the fancy car I was driving and the pile of money we'd jointly secured as projects fell away too.

Rock bottom, needing peace, I started exploring alternative ways of thinking, being and living. It was around about that time that I met a group of meditation teachers that changed my life. I saw in their eyes a peace I had never seen before. And the more I spent time with them the more it became obvious to me that their inner peace was permanent. Hungry to experience the same, I packed my bag again and headed off to meditate with them for a few months. I spent 10 weeks on the island of Patmos in Greece, followed by a further 14 weeks in the mountains of Mexico.

A total turnaround in thinking

I discovered the real cause of my problems had never been my failings at 'thinking positively'. Instead, my habit of thinking *was* the cause of my problems. When I was thinking I was missing the peace that's always present. And by learning to think less and be present, life became much more enjoyable. Since being shown this enlightening truth, I've experienced levels of peace, happiness, love and contentment beyond what I ever thought possible. With this book I hope to help you do the same.

Freedom from problems for good

Ultimately, when it comes to you enjoying life-long inner peace and happiness it's how you relate to your mind that matters. If you have to stop your negative thoughts to be at peace, then you will remain victim to the random movement of your mind forever. However, the moment you become aware of what I refer to as your Real Self, you notice there is instantly more peace than a moment prior. What's more, resting in your Real Self gives you the power to choose for a life lived in a state of permanent peace, unconditional happiness and constant contentment. Amid an ocean of what can be best described as pure, deep and unbounded Love.

Sandy Newbigging
10th October 2010

peace
for life

PEACE FOR LIFE

PART ONE

freedom from problems

PEACE FOR LIFE

CHAPTER ONE
Stop treating symptoms

Better health, peace of mind and happiness is not some far-off fantasy. Instead, it is your birthright as a human being. It is your most natural state of being because it takes effort, stress, and being out of balance to live in any other way.

It is the natural tendency of the body to heal itself and it will do so when given the chance.

Using the methods outlined in this book I regularly witness physical healings occurring, along with dramatic improvements in how people feel and the life results they enjoy. All by doing one thing: helping people to heal their Unhealthy Beliefs by getting peace with their past.

A proven method that works, fast

Through my work as a therapist at clinics, workshops and residential retreats around the world, I have developed a method that enables people to discover and resolve the, often hidden, mental and emotional causes of physical conditions, emotional issues and life problems.

My method finds what I refer to as the Root-Cause Reason (RCR), which you will learn is justifying the existence of one or more Unhealthy Beliefs. It then helps you to heal the Unhealthy Beliefs by coming to some healthier conclusions that, due to the interconnection between your mind, your body, and your world, can cause healing to naturally occur in your body and your life.

Having tracked the main beliefs causing imbalances in several hundreds of clients, I have discovered the most common Unhealthy Beliefs that I believe can cause physical problems. In this book, I will share what these beliefs are so that you can make sure you don't have any of them.

A move beyond treating surface-level symptoms

Conventional approaches to healing physical conditions often fail to deliver long-term benefits because they only treat the surface-level-physical-symptoms rather than healing the deeper underlying mental and emotional causes.

Ignoring the underlying causes is a bit like attempting to flatten a turbulent river without first removing the jagged rocks sitting below the surface; you can try all you like, but without removing the rocks it's going to make very little difference!

The mind and body are very much one. As a result, physical problems don't necessarily have purely physical causes. Due to the scientifically proven mind-body connection, mental beliefs and emotional unease can show up as physical problems too.

When you change your mind, your body responds accordingly, because the mind and body are in constant communication.

Millions of people unintentionally block their health and happiness with hidden Unhealthy Beliefs that are harmful to their bodies and lives. These beliefs put their bodies under unnecessary stress, which makes them more prone to experiencing physical 'dis-ease'. Incredibly, these beliefs also communicate with the individual cells of the body, which as you will learn, can respond by creating physical conditions that mirror the consistent messages sent to them by the mind. Furthermore, beliefs influence how you interpret life events, thus determining whether you experience a problematic or joyful life too.

The body doesn't just break and life isn't against you.

Your body is programmed for survival and will do everything it can to stay alive. What you may consider to be a 'physical problem' is in fact your body's best attempt at adapting in order to survive the mental and emotional conditions that it is subjected to during daily life.

If you have a problematic health condition then there is a reason *why*. Your body will simply keep creating the same problem until the reason for the condition is resolved. By resolving the underlying reasons *why* your problem has existed up until now, your problem simply has no alternative but to disappear for good. It just makes sense.

In my experience, the cause of many physical, emotional, and life problems exist within the more subtle realms of the mind. They are usually hidden Unhealthy Beliefs that you are unaware even exist. This can make them very difficult to find and fix – unless you know how. With this book I will be sharing a proven method for doing exactly this so you can be free from your Unhealthy Beliefs for good.

Take your healing journey to an entire new level
But the benefits of this book don't stop there. I will also be sharing ways to enjoy more inner peace and happiness by changing how you relate to your mind because, let's face it, what's the point in living a long healthy life, if you aren't enjoying it!

Relating to your mind from a more neutral perspective can reap rapid rewards. Instead of having to individually heal all of your negative beliefs and emotions so that you can *eventually* enjoy some peace, you can *immediately* connect with inner peace right now.

Take a moment to consider the implications of this remarkable possibility. You don't need to spend years trying to fix, change and improve yourself so that one day you can enjoy peace of mind. Rather, peace comes built in and enjoying your birthright can be as simple and immediate as tapping into an inner peace that is *already* present.

Stop working towards peace, and instead,
start walking the path of peace.

Healing your relationship with your mind reconnects you with ever-increasing levels of peace, happiness, love, joy and contentment. It can once and for all free you from limited thinking and enable you to enjoy the abundance that life has to offer. What's more, you can rediscover the unbounded brilliance of your Real Self – the permanent still silent awareness that exists beyond the confines of your mind.

From being your Real Self as you go about your day, you can experience life in its perfection, free from problems, whilst resting within an inner reservoir of perfect peace, for life.

About this book

Peace for Life is divided into 3 parts:

PART 1: **Freedom from problems**
PART 2: **Peace with your past**
PART 3: **Enjoying peace for life**

In Part 1, I will introduce why enjoying better health, peace of mind and happiness is your birthright, share some inspiring real-life success stories, and reveal my seven self-healing secrets. Knowing these secrets can help you to harness your own self-healing capabilities and cultivate the right mindset for enjoying a problem free life.

In Part 2 I then help you to discover any Unhealthy Beliefs that might be secretly making you sick. To make things easy for you, I share the most common Unhealthy Beliefs that I've found to cause problems. Once you find your Unhealthy Beliefs, we then progress on to help you to come to some new, healthier conclusions. This helps you to be at peace when thinking about past events and can also help your body heal, be emotionally liberating and help you make positive changes to your life.

In Part 3 we then turn our attention to you enjoying inner peace and happiness, for life! We leave *changing the mind* behind for a while and venture into the perhaps unknown territory of *changing your relationship with your mind*. The purpose of Part 3 is to reconnect you with your Real Self and the peace that's always present. At this point, if you are able to keep an open mind and play with the games I share; then *peace for life* can be your reward.

TOP TIP
Finish the book!

You bought this book because you want better health, peace of mind and happiness. It can help you get what you want but you must start by reading the entire book. To stop half way is to be within a hairs-breadth of enjoying the most wonderful life, but turn away at the last moment. Whatever you do, make sure you read Part 3 of the book. I want you to discover the peace that's always present.

For the best results, please...

Be innocent
The chances are you've read other 'health' books and this isn't your very first attempt at healing your physical condition or life problems. Most people that use my method have tried other approaches and been let down. However, irrespective of what's happened in the past, you need to leave the past where it belongs – in the past!

I encourage you to trust the process, suspend judgement and jump in with as much childlike curiosity and innocence as you can muster. Your mind, body and universe respond quickest to you being one-pointed by taking action without tentativeness. Leave doubt at the door when using the methods outlined in this book and do your best to not let scepticism steal your success.

Be willing to change

Although, in reality, most people's comfort zones are pretty uncomfortable, self-limiting beliefs and health problems can become familiar. Be completely honest with yourself when considering these questions:

Are you willing to draw a line in the sand and step out into perhaps unfamiliar territory? Are you willing to do things differently? Are you willing to trust the process, even if at the start, some parts may seem pointless? And are you willing to do whatever it takes to build momentum towards new healthier habits?

If yes, then great! You are reading the right book.

Be clear on what you want

For you to get the results you want it is vital that you begin with a clear intention. Below are three questions to help you gain clarity on what you want:

1. What physical condition(s), emotional issue(s) or life problem(s) do you want to heal?
2. What is your heart's greatest desire? By that I mean, what do you want more than anything else?
3. How will you know healing has happened and you've got the results you wanted?

Be easy on yourself

Reading a book like this can make you aware of how your thoughts, emotions and lifestyle may be negatively impacting your physical health. But what's very important to keep in mind is that although your health *is* your responsibility, you have not intentionally *done it to yourself* and it is not your fault. The ultimate cause of your thinking patterns, emotional habits and behaviours exist in the more subtle realms of your mind. Blaming yourself or feeling guilty about what's happening to your body does not help it heal, quite the opposite in fact. Be easy on yourself and gently make whatever positive changes you can.

Finally, be committed

Do you really want to experience life differently? Are you willing to persist until you get the results you want?

People who have had complete remissions from illnesses or transformed their life for the better have made it their number one priority, for as long as it has taken. I didn't *do it in a week* and I continue to practice the techniques shared within this book.

If you can follow instructions, remain open-minded and trust your first answers to the questions you will be asked, you massively improve the chances of enjoying similar benefits to the success stories you are about to read in Chapter 2…

CHAPTER TWO
Self-healing success stories

Miracles *do* happen! I've been lucky enough to witness people from around the world heal a wide variety of physical, emotional and life problems that more conventional thinking would suggest were impossible to cure.

Over the past few years, people experiencing the methods shared in this book have reported improvements with the following problems: acid reflux, acne, addictions, allergies, anxiety, asthma, arthritis, back problems, chronic pain, constipation, depression, diabetes, eating disorders, eczema, fatigue, food intolerances, headaches, hearing loss, hyperhydrosis, insomnia, irritable bowel syndrome, low self-esteem, M.E., migraines, money issues, panic attacks, psoriasis, phobias, relationship difficulties, thyroid problems, weight gain, and more.

Cultivate the right mindset

To increase your confidence in what you are about to learn, please read through the real life self-healing success stories presented in the following pages. Not only do they make for highly inspirational reading, but they can also help you to develop the belief that self-healing is not only possible, but also inevitable, which is paramount for activating your body's inbuilt self-healing capabilities.

BENEFIT #1
Pain free without painkillers

The body can speak the mind. If something causes you emotional pain, then it can eventually lead to physical pain. I've seen chronic pain vanish instantly when a person finds peace with their past.

Meet John, who had back pain...
"Ever since a car accident over two years ago I had been suffering from a painful lower back. After a conversation with Sandy we discovered the root-cause of why my back was vulnerable in the first place, which linked back to when my dad went into hospital for a few weeks when I was a child. When I resolved it, the pain went away

immediately. That night I slept through with no pain killers (for the first time in over two years) and got up the next morning and did yoga!"

Meet Gail, who had painful knees...

"I had been suffering with very painful and swollen knees for many months so I met up with Sandy to receive a mind detox consultation. I was amazed by the results. The pain eased immediately and by the following day the swelling had gone down and I was able to wear my beloved three-inch heels again. I am still pain free and trotting around in my heels. Mind Detox is fantastic."

Meet Kate, who also had knee problems...

"After a kneecap dislocation, I found myself experiencing extreme pain every time I tried to move my knee, making physiotherapy, and therefore recovery, impossible. Through working with a pain specialist physiotherapist I came to realise that my knee did not actually hurt at all, that there was a psychological reason for the pain I was feeling. I had one session with Sandy where he quickly identified that the original dislocation had reminded me of a traumatic event from my childhood and the memory was manifesting itself as pain in my knee.

After only one session I returned to physiotherapy and was able to get on an exercise bike. I regained the ability to walk soon after. I truly believe that if I had undergone traditional therapy, probably coupled with the anti-

depressants my doctor had been recommending, it would have taken many months before I recovered.

Sandy's method is good at drawing out deeply suppressed feelings and dissolving them. I felt euphoric after my session, like a huge weight had been lifted from my head. I would recommend mind detox to anyone suffering from a physical condition that won't heal."

Meet Debbie, who had period pains for 30 years...

"I had been suffering from period pains ever since I'd started my menstrual cycle at age 13. I experienced Sandy's method when I was 43 and wish I hadn't waited so long! Every month I was left with no energy and felt out of control and resentful. I discovered during my Mind Detox consultation that I had had my first period on my 13th birthday and it made me feel dirty, uncomfortable, sad, scared and unloved. This emotionally-linked with an earlier event aged four when I had felt the same in relation to whether my dad loved me. When I recognized that he had loved me my whole life, all the other negative emotions cleared instantly. Two weeks later I had my first pain-free period in 30 years!"

TOP TIP
Saying the unsayable

One way to curb chronic pain is to heal events in your life when you've not been able to speak your mind or feel your feelings. By saying the *unsayable* and feeling the *unfeelable* once and for all - in relation to people or events in your past - stored emotional stress can be released, along with physical pain.

BENEFIT #2
Loving the skin you're in

Skin can be one of the first physical signs of a person having unresolved emotional issues below the surface. The nature of the skin condition that occurs is often symbolic. By that, hyper-skin-sensitivity in the form of eczema can be the result of separation anxiety (whereby the skin is increasing its ability to 'reach out and touch/find' the lost person, place, event or thing). Or in cases of psoriasis where the skin is producing extra cells, it is often the result of an external attack, such as bullying or near-death experience, causing the body to produce an extra thick line of defence against the perceived threat.

As the human body 'grows a new skin' by regenerating the skin cells every month or so, healing can occur very quickly once the reason for the skin condition is resolved.

Meet Melissa, who had eczema...
"*I was a complete self-diagnosed stress head until I met Sandy. I can confidently say that I am a much more*

relaxed person now and a number of the negative health side effects of the stress have completely disappeared. I also benefited from the drastically improved appearance of my skin when I resolved the Root-Cause Reason for my eczema (which stemmed back to an event that happened when I was a child). Thanks very much, I feel brilliant!"

BENEFIT #3
Brilliantly working bowels!

The brain and bowels are very much emotionally connected. Similarly to the skin, the bowels are prone to speaking the mind in rather symbolic ways. For instance, people finding certain events in their life 'hard to digest' can suffer with digestive problems. Others experiencing excessive stress or anxiety often end up with the additional concern of needing to find toilets quickly due to their chronic diarrhoea. People who have suffered loss in their life and experience difficulties letting go are often more likely to become constipated as their bowels stop letting go too.

Getting peace with the past using the methods in this book can help on all three counts, allowing for better functioning bowels.

Meet Tracey, who had irritable bowel syndrome...
"I was totally stressed out, overweight, constipated, had odema in my legs so bad that I couldn't kneel down, had no

self-confidence, and sweated uncontrollably if anyone spoke to me. I am now much more confidant, 12 pounds lighter, with no odema, no constipation and no sweating! Sandy's method is fantastic and I can only thank you from the bottom of my heart – I am a new woman!"

Meet Ian, who had chronic constipation...

"I had suffered from badly working bowels ever since I was a child. I worked with Sandy when I was 34 and discovered that I had a hidden belief that it wasn't safe to go to the toilet. To be honest, once we healed that out-of-date belief I immediately had to go to the toilet as my constipation had ceased to exist! One month on and my bowels are functioning brilliantly, and I've even lost about a stone (6.4kgs) in weight, without dieting, now my body knows it's safe to let go!"

BENEFIT #4
Life-changing weight loss

Excess weight is often a symptom of one or more physical and/or emotional problem(s). Enjoying a healthy weight requires you to explore the reasons why your body has felt the need to adapt by gaining weight. Then be willing to make a few changes to the physical and emotional conditions in which your body exists. Doing so can naturally cause your body to adapt again, but this time, by losing weight.

Meet Susan who was struggling with her weight...
"I had gained weight in my twenties, but didn't understand why. Whatever I did to lose it didn't make much difference. When working with Sandy I found a connection between when the weight gain happened and what had been going on in my life at the time. It became clear to me that the extra weight was my body's way of protecting me from the conflict that was happening in my family. When I let go of the unresolved emotions relating to the difficult time in my life, I immediately began to lose weight. It was magic!"

BENEFIT #5
No sweat!

Often linked with anxiety and anger, my method has been used to successfully treat excessive sweating. In the majority of cases, the Root-Cause Event is a time when lots of attention was on the person and they didn't know what to do. This caused the body to have a shock and go into panic-mode any time similar events happen again. It is also common for the perspiring person to have felt unfairly treated too, causing an undercurrent of anger.

Meet Alistair, who sweated excessively...
"Despite being a very fit and healthy Royal Marine, I had to hide the fact that I sweated uncontrollably. I had to always wear dark coloured clothes, sleep on a towel and

couldn't go for the promotion I wanted because sweating was seen as a sign of being unfit. Sandy helped me get to parts of my mind I didn't know existed. We found a memory of a time at school when a teacher shouted at me unfairly and I felt angry that I was made to look stupid. When I achieved peace with the past event the excessive sweating that I'd had for years calmed down. I am now in control of the condition and able to get on with my life with greater confidence and peace of mind."

BENEFIT #6
No more migraines

Meet Sophie, who had migraines...
"For years I had suffered with debilitating migraines. Working with Sandy helped me to find what had been 'on my mind' (albeit my unconscious mind!) the entire time. I was able to change the beliefs that were causing me to feel so negative towards myself, and clear the blocks that had been preventing me from making necessary changes to the way I'd been living life. I've not had a single migraine or headache since. My relationships with my friends have improved and my fears around having a family of my own have disappeared. I'm now very happily married and we are even expecting our first baby. Truly life-changing!"

Meet Rachel, who suffered from regular migraines...
"I had been suffering from regular migraines for years. During my consultation with Sandy I discovered and

healed the emotional cause of the migraines, which stemmed back to when a friend committed suicide. This also linked to an earlier event when a family member died suddenly. Amazingly, my headache went away immediately when I gave myself permission to be at peace with the passing of those I love. I've not had a migraine since."

BENEFIT #7
A sweeter life, naturally

I nearly fell of my chair when I heard about this success story from a Mind Detox Method (MDM) Practitioner working in Mexico:

Meet Rosa, who had diabetes...
"I had severe diabetes and my blood count was 300. The day after my Mind Detox consultation my blood count had dropped to 160! And now, three months after the consultation, my doctor has completely taken me off the medication."

BENEFIT #8
Bad behaviours be gone

Destructive behaviours such as phobias, addictions and compulsive disorders can be a thing of the past using the methods outlined in this book. Mainly because your beliefs determine your emotions and your emotions drive your behaviours. By changing your emotionally fuelled beliefs, you can more easily and naturally behave however you want.

Meet Juliet, who was a compulsive cleaner...

"Everything had to be immaculate. I was missing out on going for walks and playing outside with my child because I couldn't stand dirt. Working with Sandy I discovered that I had made an unconscious connection between dirt and feelings of vulnerability. This meant anytime I saw anything unclean I would immediately feel vulnerable and need to either clean it or run away from it. When I resolved the cause for this unconscious connection I immediately became able to enjoy being around mud and all things messy! This has freed me up to enjoy family life more, which even includes the occasional pottery lesson!"

Meet Elizabeth, who couldn't travel abroad...

"I had not been abroad on holiday for 20 years because I got really ill on the return flight from my last holiday and was convinced the same thing was going to happen again.

A few weeks before my holiday I spent a couple of hours with Sandy and he helped me discover the real reasons why I was so frightened about getting ill when travelling. This not only helped me to enjoy the weeks leading up to my holidays without worry, but also let me enjoy the flight without being ill and without having to take medication.

I now fly abroad and within the UK quite frequently and without incident and thoroughly enjoy it. My whole life has changed as I use the techniques Sandy gave me whenever I feel stressed and it works. I can't emphasise enough how beneficial it would be to anyone with any kind of issues be they mental or physical to spend some time with Sandy - it can change your life forever."

BENEFIT #9
Cool, calm and confident

I bet you are much more confident than you think! Are you confident making a cup of tea, cleaning the house or doing a hobby you love? Of course you are. This is because confidence is context dependent. In other words, there is no such thing as 'unconfident people', only those who experience negative thoughts and emotions when faced with certain life events. Confidence is the natural way you feel when you are NOT thinking and feeling negatively.

People with low confidence often worry about what other people think about them. So the antidote to low confidence includes learning to love yourself more fully so you don't *need* to be liked by others.

Meet Annette, who had low self-esteem...
"I had so many issues to sort out that if I just got rid of one it would have been a bonus. I have found out, using

Sandy's method, that by getting to the root-cause, all the related problems tumble away - and it works. It is magic. I used to think that I wasn't good enough, that everyone I love leaves me etc but now, for the very first time in my whole life, I KNOW I AM PERFECT!"

TOP TIP
Using your eyes for a change

Due to the mind-body connection, you are physically wired to feel certain ways when you do certain things with your body. Simply putting your shoulders back, puffing your chest up and out, having a solid stance (so you are stable on your feet), breathing in a deep and balanced way, and putting a big smile on your face can all help you cultivate confidence. Not only that, but there is even a way of using your eyes that automatically causes you to feel cool, calm and confident in seconds. Check out 'Appendix 3: 3C Vision' on page 222 for full instructions.

BENEFIT #10
Peace for life!

The Unhealthy Beliefs associated with unresolved emotional events can put the body-mind into a perpetual state of stress (known as fight or flight). This can make a person more inclined to constantly search their environment for potential threats. Over think, and experience chronic anxiety.

Meet Jill, who had debilitating anxiety...

"I was getting daily bouts of anxiety, these were debilitating and stopped me doing ordinary every day things. I would shake, feel sick, over-eat to stop the nausea and rush about like a headless chicken not really getting anywhere. Since using the methods taught by Sandy I have not had any anxiety, have much more energy, been more focused and got more done. My life, and consequently the lives of those around me, has become calmer and happier. I laugh a lot more and I'm sleeping better. Old behaviour patterns and past traumas are now a thing of the past as I learn to live in and enjoy each moment."

Changing your relationship with your mind (described in detail in Part 3) can also yield massive benefits. By choosing to prioritize your peace and taking steps to relate to your mind in a more neutral way, you can enjoy remarkable results.

Meet Jen, who suffered from extreme anxiety...

"I was always worried that something bad was going to happen and anxious about what other people thought of me. It was a horrible strain on my body. I was totally tense and sometimes felt I couldn't breathe properly. I would get the shakes because I was so nervous and on edge.

My neck and shoulders were in pain and I had even started going grey in my twenties due to stress.

Learning meditation with Sandy totally changed my perspective on life. I now see the world for the first time through awakened eyes. I've learnt how to take a step back from the commotion of my mind and to simply watch it. Making this shift helped me to realise that I am the peaceful awareness that is aware of my thoughts and emotions. What a relief. The real me is at peace and I didn't even know it! Thanks Sandy for helping me to meet my Real Self again, to stop worrying so much about what people think about me and to enjoy peace for life!"

Meet Jem, who had problematic panic attacks...

"For years, I struggled with panic attacks, constant anxiety and low self-esteem. But now, as I am writing this, I am filled with a sense of silent contentment. I no longer live in the past and I am not stressed about the future. I am amazed that I am actually experiencing peace, happiness and joy! I feel as though I have found my Real Self and each minute I am falling more and more in love with who I am."

Meet Bianca, who had considered ending her life...

"Going beyond my unhealthy beliefs has taught me how to live life with very little effort and to enjoy it. I can literally feel the warmth and energy circulate every square inch of my body. From wanting to end my life a few weeks ago, to discovering joy, freedom and peace - that's quite a result!"

27

Having read these success stories, you are probably becoming increasingly excited about learning and using the same techniques that helped these happy people enjoy such great benefits. I promise I will share the actual methods with you soon but, before I do, I want to let you in on a few secrets that sit at the heart of many of these miraculous success stories...

CHAPTER THREE
Seven self-healing secrets

Knowing the following self-healing secrets can help you to access your own self-healing capabilities. The secrets, (called 'secrets' because few people know them), explain why physical problems don't necessarily have purely physical causes, how your emotional wellbeing and your physical wellness are inextricably linked, and why it is possible to heal your body and your life by changing your mind.

Working in accordance with these self-healing secrets has been instrumental in helping me to develop the right mindset for helping others. I believe they can help you to take control of your physical and emotional destiny, be free from chronic stress, and enjoy a more fulfilling life. Ready to learn the first secret? Let's begin!

SECRET #1
Your body *is* your mind

What your mind believes, perceives and experiences has the potential of being sent to your entire body causing physical responses.

A commonly held misconception in the western world is that the mind and body are separate entities: that there are physical problems and there are mental or emotional problems. However, the mind and body is very much one entity. Mental stress and unresolved emotional unease has the potential to impact upon many aspects of the physical body, often showing up as physical conditions.

The mind-body connection has been known for centuries, but it is only in recent years that so many scientific studies have been able to prove how thoughts and emotions affect the body:

If you're grateful... then you almost double certain aspects of your immune system, heal more quickly due to higher oxygenation of the tissues, and positively impact the 'coherence' of your heart rhythms - which can have a positive knock-on effect with many of the other essential organs too.

If you're angry... then researchers at Ohio State University found you get a surge in cytokines, the immune molecules that trigger inflammation. High levels of cytokines are linked with arthritis, diabetes, heart disease and cancer.

If you're jealous... then your body ends up suffering from increased blood pressure, heart rate, adrenalin levels, and a weakened immunity.

If you're in love... then you increase the levels of nerve growth factor according to research at the University of Pavia in Italy. Enhanced nerve growth helps restore the nervous system and improves memory. Love has also been linked with pain relief, healthier hearts and living longer.

If you're stressed-out... then a harmful concoction of stress hormones, including adrenaline and norepinephrine, can end up circulating through your body. Over time, stress hormones like these have been found to compromise immune system, weaken organs, cause the body to turn off long-term building and repair projects, speed up the aging process and make the body more prone to develop chronic illness.

And the list goes on and on...
Your mind is linked with your Autonomic Nervous System (ANS), which regulates your heartbeat, blood pressure, digestion and metabolism, along with many

more of the 'automatic' bodily functions.

Obvious autonomic mind-body connection responses include getting a red face when embarrassed, your mouth watering when you think of a food you love, and experiencing butterflies in your stomach when you're feeling nervous or excited. Even sexual arousal requires the mind and body to communicate! Although we generally take these everyday physical reactions for granted, it's useful to take a moment to appreciate what's actually happening.

Your embarrassed red face requires thousands of chemical reactions to take place within your body along with the diversion of blood flow to your skin. Sensations of nervousness in your stomach is the blood draining from the stomach lining as it heads to the outer regions of the body to help you resist or run from the perceived external threat. And when it comes to sexual arousal... well, we all know that a range of physical responses can occur if certain thoughts occur!

Chemical messengers of the mind
Many of these examples of the mind-body connection are possible due to evidence of the mind being found to exist in the cells of your body. When you think, neuropeptides (also known as "the molecules of emotion") are released into your bloodstream, which

in turn can affect the functioning of your entire body by communicating with your individual cells.

Now there are very few places on your body that you can cut yourself where you wouldn't bleed. Similarly, there is virtually nowhere in your body where you don't find neuropeptides. The body is literally riddled with the chemical messengers of your thoughts. So much so that it is scientifically accurate to say the state of your body is quite literally a physical manifestation of your mind.

Yes, that's right. Your body is a physical manifestation of your mind.

Stop to consider all the physical reactions that happen as a result of what's happening in your thoughts and emotions. And you can't help but begin to question if your chronic back pain, skin condition or digestive disorder is the result of a purely physical cause. The implications of the mind-body connection are massive when it comes to understanding why people get physical problems.

This is especially so when you explore the extent to which your beliefs are not only known by the cells of your body, but are constantly causing physical changes to occur. More about this soon, but first...

LET'S PLAY A GAME
Monitoring the mind-body

For the next 24 hours, be highly vigilant to the physical reactions that occur in your body when thinking about different things in your mind, (or when experiencing different situations).

Notice what happens within your body when you:

- ✓ *Think about certain memories*
- ✓ *Think about someone you dislike compared to someone you love dearly*
- ✓ *Think about different future scenarios that you are excited about compared to ones you're worried about*
- ✓ *Find something funny and laugh*
- ✓ *Find something sad and cry*
- ✓ *When you criticize someone/something*
- ✓ *When you praise and appreciate someone/something*
- ✓ *Experience different external situations – like being stuck in traffic, being hugged, watching a movie etc.*

A vital first step in self-healing

The first step in intentionally self-healing (I say intentionally, because you are unintentionally self-healing all the time!), is to notice first hand, in your own personal life experience, that your thoughts and emotions *are* impacting your body.

Becoming aware of this means you move from being

oblivious to the ongoing, behind the scenes, impact of the mind-body connection, to a simple appreciation that it is happening. Although a simple step, believe it or not, this is a **massive leap** towards taking charge of your physical destiny.

When you fully appreciate that your thoughts and emotions impact upon what happens within your body, you naturally find yourself in a far better position to actively influence your physical health and well-being.

SECRET #2
Your beliefs become your body

Unhealthy Beliefs can manifest physically as an unhealthy body.

Your beliefs impact your body
Beliefs can impact biology due to the interconnection of the mind and body. Your beliefs are the conclusions that you've come to throughout your life about your body, your personality, your capabilities, self-worth, lovability, safety and so on.

Beliefs have been found to have the power to influence many aspects of a person's physical functioning, including digestion, immune system, blood pressure and even the DNA.

Impacts of the belief-body connection range from everyday physical responses to more life threatening results; in a very real way, your beliefs become your biology. Recognising the impact of your beliefs can help you to increase confidence in your own self-healing capabilities.

The miracle in your mouth

When you think about a food you like your body gets ready to eat it. Your salivary glands immediately go to work producing a fluid composed of water, mucus, proteins, mineral salts and amylase, an enzyme that breaks down starches.

Incredibly, your body can react differently towards foods you like compared to foods you dislike. When you think about a food you don't like your body produces less saliva, making it more difficult to swallow the food you *believe* you don't like. Two very different physical responses, yet the only way the body knows to respond differently is via the beliefs you have about the different kinds of foods. Amazing!

Clockwork orange

Perhaps even more amazing are the experiences of some people with multiple personality disorders. There are documented cases of the same person having different physical conditions depending on the prominent personality at any given time. In a particular case, one personality was highly allergic to oranges and the other could eat them with no allergic reaction whatsoever. And in another case, one personality needed glasses to see, whereas the other had perfect 20-20 vision. In both cases, the *cause* of the differences between the personalities existed in the mind, not the body.

Placebo power

More evidence of how beliefs impact the body is the global phenomenon of the placebo effect. The placebo effect happens when a person takes a fake pill believing it is the *real* pill, but ends up getting better anyway. In the thousands of documented cases worldwide, it is clearly the person's belief that the fake pill will work, not the ingredients of the pill, which causes healing to occur.

Just as powerful though is the harmful effect of the nocebo. The nocebo effect is the opposite of the placebo, whereby a person's beliefs play a role in them getting sick and, in some cases, even dying.

Catching a cold

I used to get ill a couple times every winter when I would 'catch a cold'. Then one day I discovered some compelling evidence that proved to me (my mind) that it was impossible to 'catch a cold' and, guess what, I have never caught one since. Is this a coincidence? I don't believe so.

The clock is ticking

Or have you ever heard about people being told that they only have a finite time to live, say three months, and they've ended up dying three months to the day of the terminal diagnosis? Is this a coincidence? Again, I don't believe so. In these common examples, I believe it is beliefs becoming the body.

Having worked with hundreds of people to help them change beliefs, I've discovered two types of Unhealthy Beliefs that impact the body:

Body Beliefs and Stress Beliefs

Body Beliefs directly relate to the physical functioning of the body. They are conclusions you've come to about your body that eventually become self-fulfilling prophecies, such as, *'I always get the flu in winter'*, or another common one: *'I will gain weight with age.'*

This one actually caught me out

Growing up I was constantly told that I could eat whatever I wanted, but when I hit 30 years old I would need to be careful because I would get fat. Amazingly, within days of turning 30 I began gaining weight despite my diet or exercise regime being the same as it had always been. After a few weeks I realised I must have picked up a Body Belief about gaining weight with age. So I set about doing everything I could not to change my body, but my mind.

To help disprove the unhealthy Body Belief I gave myself the goal of noticing all the people in my life who were older than 30 that had *not* gained weight. This helped me to naturally heal the Unhealthy Belief because my mind now had lots of evidence to prove that it is normal to maintain a slim body the older I get. Within a couple of weeks my body was back to my normal weight and I could continue enjoying freedom with food.

Beliefs stressing the body out of balance

The other type of beliefs I observe in people suffering from physical conditions is what I call *Stress Beliefs*. These are the kinds of beliefs that cause people to experience high levels of stress, unease and angst during daily life.

'I'm not safe', 'I'm bad', 'It's my fault', 'I'm not good enough', or 'I'm abandoned', are just a few examples. Amongst other unhealthy side effects, beliefs like these can cause your mind to constantly search your life for potential threats, leading to your body being in a perpetual state of fight-flight survival mode, and the increased likelihood of physical problems.

Meet Ros, who had abdominal pain... *"I had been sent from one hospital department to the other over several years, no doctor seemed to be able discover the cause of my abdominal pain until I saw Sandy. He helped me to get to the real emotional root of the problem, and the pain that had given me years of agony disappeared. All the other associated physical and emotional problems disappeared as well. Initially I was half waiting for them to return, but two years on I'm still feeling great!"*

Ros is a perfect example of how quickly the body can heal when you change Unhealthy Beliefs in the mind. Her hidden belief was that she was *abandoned*. We discovered she formed that belief aged four when she managed to escape from her nursery, and run home, only to find an empty house. Her belief that she'd been abandoned was causing her intense negative emotions, which were stressful on her body, and manifesting as chronic physical pain.

> *By changing your beliefs you can cause changes to occur within your body.*

Now, the truth is she wasn't abandoned, in fact, *she'd* run away from nursery without telling anyone! But her belief that she was abandoned was enough to negatively impact her health, for years! When she found peace with her past by remembering her mum came home a few minutes later and she wasn't abandoned because she'd run away, the negative emotion cleared, along with the physical pain.

TOP TIP
Befriend your beliefs

Your mind wants to prove your beliefs right. So if you have a belief that you are abandoned, then your mind will do everything it can to help you be abandoned again and again! If you believe life is hard then life *will* be difficult. Or if you have the belief you aren't safe, then your mind will help you find evidence that proves you're in danger. Not because your mind is against you, quite the opposite – it's trying to help you be right!

Peace for Life can help you to discover and heal any Unhealthy Beliefs that may be counterproductive to your health and happiness. Harnessing your self-healing capabilities requires you to befriend your beliefs by making sure they are working in your best interest.

To discover beliefs that may be impacting upon your body, it is very useful to begin to see the symbolic way that your body speaks your mind. Because as you do, you can discover that...

SECRET #3
Your body is not against you

Symptoms most people consider to be physical problems can in fact be your body's best attempt at staying alive.

Survival is the primary goal of the human body. It is not designed to just break, malfunction or get 'sick' *without good reason*. Instead it is constantly doing everything in its power to adapt to, and survive, the inner and outer conditions it is experiencing during daily life. This happens because your body follows the orders given to it by your mind. More specifically, the individual cells that make up your body are so intelligent they are constantly adjusting themselves to the environment in which they 'think' they exist.

Adapting to the chemical climate
It works like this: Your mind interprets whatever is happening in the external environment and then your brain releases chemical messengers of your thoughts (neuropeptides) into the blood, which tell the cells what adjustments they need to make in order to best survive the *perceived* environment. So in the same way you would adapt to a change in the weather when it rains by putting a rain jacket on, your individual cells adapt to their chemical climate too and the chemical messengers they are being flooded with on a daily basis.

The body speaks the mind

Your mind-body is communicating this way now. The millions of cells that make up your body are listening to your mind and responding accordingly. This means that if you are being loving, quite literally, your heart is experiencing love. If you feel unsupported, your knees feel it. Or if you're feeling fear, your entire body is on red alert. The result? Physical symptoms are often highly symbolic, as the body does a brilliant job at speaking the mind.

Cast your mind back

Remember Alex, who had excessive sweating. We discovered during our consultations that his sweat was, in his words, 'anger bubbling up inside'. When he let go of the pent-up anger, the body stopped sweating excessively. Or Ian, whose constipation was the result of his body believing it wasn't safe to go to the toilet after an 'accident' as a child. His body was trying to help him by becoming constipated! Other examples that spring to mind include:

Anna, who had psoriasis...

"My legs had been completely covered with psoriasis for over 25 years. I discovered using Sandy's method that it was my body's way of protecting me from a series of external threats, including bullying, that I had encountered during my teenage years. Within a few weeks of healing the fears associated with the past bullying, the skin on my legs was back to normal."

Meet Julie, who had lost her hearing...

"About 18 months ago I was diagnosed with Meniere's disease, a condition which affects the inner ear with excess fluid build-up leading to debilitating attacks of severe vertigo, vomiting, tinnitus and eventually damage to the hearing causing permanent hearing loss. Gradually my hearing in my right ear had deteriorated to the point of fluctuating between severe loss and moderate loss. I had needed to resort to getting a hearing aid fitted.

I attended the Mind Detox Method Practitioner training with Sandy in Australia. During the course Sandy demonstrated a one-on-one session with me in which I discovered a memory of my parents divorcing when I was six. I was scared at the time about not knowing what was going to happen and I felt unloved. Sandy helped me recognize that life did go on and that I was loved.

After our session I kept forgetting to wear my hearing aid. I didn't think much of it until I was doing the meditation course with Sandy the following weekend and I could clearly hear a conversation on the other side of the room. At first I doubted it, as I could not normally hear a conversation that far away, even with my hearing aid. That night to my surprise I put my headphones in my right ear first and found I could hear! Normally it would be muffled but this time it was loud and clear. I had my hearing back and I sense the Meniere's has gone too! So perhaps, what I needed to HEAR the most was that I'm loved! Thank you so much Sandy, I'm now able to hear that I'm loved and so much more. I am forever grateful."

Also, meet Sandra, who had period pains for 20 years... "*Ever since I was a teenager I had suffered from intense cramps every month. I thought it was just something I had to grin and bear... until I heard about Sandy's method. We discovered an event in my past where I had lost someone I loved dearly. When I resolved the resistance to letting go of that person, I immediately felt a release in my body. I have experienced hardly any period pain since.*"

Sandra was resisting the loss of someone she loved and her body was resisting letting go each month – in the physical manifestation of period pains. As you can see from these real-life examples, the human body is constantly adapting to survive in light of the climate of your mind. By changing your mind for the better, your body can naturally change again, but this time by functioning in a more desirable way.

Enjoying this book?
Due to the body's natural tendency to respond positively to positive messages, simply reading a book like this can potentially benefit your health in miraculous ways. Amazing, isn't it!

LET'S EXPLORE
Your body speaks your mind
Consider how your body may be speaking your mind through the creation of your current physical condition. Just for now, let go of any medical labels

you may have been given, and instead, explore the physical condition from a fresh perspective. Very useful questions to consider are:

✓ *What is happening within my body i.e. what is my body actually doing?*
✓ *How might the physical conditions be an attempt to adapt, be safe and/or survive my past or current life circumstances?*
✓ *If the physical condition was trying to send a symbolic message to me, what might it be saying?*
✓ *If the physical condition is a negative emotion, what emotion would it be?*
✓ *How might my body be mirroring my life?*
✓ *Taking account of what's happened in my life, how might my body today be a physical manifestation of my past?*
✓ *What was happening in my life during the 12 to 18 months leading up to when I first noticed the physical condition? What bad things were happening? What good things were happening? What problematic situation was resolved?*

This is an awareness-raising exercise; giving you the opportunity to explore whether there may be any possible mind-based causes to your physical condition. If you think you've found a possible cause, then hopefully the rest of this book can help you take positive steps towards self-healing.

SECRET #4
Resistance is bad for your health

Resisting life is the ultimate cause for almost all pain, toxic emotions and harmful forms of stress.

The result of regular resistance
Although short bouts of stress can actually boost immunity and raise cancer-fighting molecules, being in a perpetual state of stress is a very different story. Your body ends up turning off long-term building and repair projects, speeds up the aging process and weakens its immunity. Not only that, numerous scientific studies have found evidence that firmly links negative emotions with the onset of arthritis, diabetes, heart disease, cancer and other problems.

According to Stanford University Medical School, the Centres for Disease Control and Prevention in Atlanta (CDC), and numerous health experts, the main cause of health problems on the planet is stress. Research by the cellular biologist Dr Bruce Lipton suggested that over '95% of all illness occurs because of stress in the body's autonomic nervous system'. These findings all point to one very simple strategy for self-healing:

To increase health, we must reduce stress.

The root-cause of stress

However, in my opinion, it is neither the stress nor negative emotions that are the *ultimate cause* of many physical and emotional problems. Rather a person's resistance to life. Resistance not only causes the body stress, but is highly instrumental in whether a person feels negative emotions, or not.

Experiencing anger, sadness, fear, guilt or grief is only possible if you resist something in your past, present or future. Sadness is usually the result of resisting something in your past, whereas resisting the possibility of something bad happening in the future usually causes fear and anxiety. Irrespective of the emotion, resistance is the underlying cause.

What makes things worse for the body is the fact that most people would prefer to not experience negative emotions, so end up not only resisting life, but their emotions too! I often see this leading to a never-ending vicious cycle of a person resisting more and more day-by-day; putting their body under ever-increasing levels of stress. No wonder this compounded stress often ends up with people experiencing physical disease!

Fortunately, it is never life events that cause you stress or make you feel bad, but rather your resistance to what's happened/happening that does. Which ultimately means you have a choice. By not resisting life, stress is reduced massively and negative emotions cease to exist. To be immediately replaced with feelings of inner peace, gratitude and contentment, which are, incidentally, emotions that have all been found to aid the healing process.

From problems to peace with a new perspective

Most therapy clients I meet are resisting something. If they weren't, there would be no reason for them to work with me because everything would be OK! And by using the Mind Detox Method, I've helped them find places in their life where they've been resisting and, during the course of the consultations helped them move from a place of resistance to acceptance.

By finding the subtle (often hidden) resistances in your life and moving from a place of resistance to acceptance you can significantly reduce the amount of stress your body experiences. The less stress the more healing that occurs, not to mention that you feel much more peaceful, contented and happy.

But what if something bad is happening?

Do you just accept it? Yes, accept it, but accepting it doesn't mean you can't change it. Accepting it just means you don't cause yourself unnecessary stress and suffering whilst you go about changing whatever isn't acceptable to you. When you are less stressed and not experiencing negative emotions you have more inner peace, mental clarity and confidence. From that more peaceful and intuitive perspective, you become a very powerful and effective person. You are able to choose to change your current circumstances if they are not acceptable to you. The only difference is that you can make changes now without having to experience any negative emotions to justify your choices or actions. You simply decide for something different and welcome whatever happens next.

Life-changing question
So if you are currently experiencing a physical condition or know that you often find yourself feeling negative emotions such as anger, sadness, fear or loneliness, then there is a very important question you must ask yourself:

What in my life am I resisting?

Explore this question further by considering:

- ✓ *Am I resisting the way I've been treated by a family member, friend or colleague?*
- ✓ *Am I resisting the job that I do, my bank balance, or any other aspect of my life?*
- ✓ *Am I resisting my physical health?*
- ✓ *Should certain things in my life have turned out differently?*
- ✓ *Do I still feel bad when I think about things that have happened in the past?*
- ✓ *Do I feel discontentment with any areas of my life?*

Answering these questions can help you to highlight the areas of your life that you might be resisting. Remember, resistance is stressful for the body and the body heals best when it rests. Resistance also causes negative emotions so peace for life comes from learning to resist life less. Be super attentive to what you might be resisting and note what you discover in a journal so you can rise above resistance for better health, peace of mind and happiness.

SECRET #5
Cure the hidden Root-Cause Reasons

The cause of your resistance usually exists in the hidden parts of your mind. This can make it hard to stop resisting life – unless you know how.

Secret 4 shared how resistance is often the *ultimate cause* of physical conditions. But what's important to appreciate about resistance is that it is often not intentional and very much the result of what's going on in the more subtle, hidden, parts of your mind.

Most people I meet are usually aware of the surface-level-results of resistance i.e. that they feel sad about the past, worried about the future or stressed about what's happening today - but live unaware of the underlying reasons why they feel the way they do.

Shining a light on the hidden parts of your mind
Tune into your mind by noticing your thoughts. The ones you can 'hear' have made their way up to your conscious awareness. They exist in what's called your conscious mind. However, there is also a level to your mind that operates below the surface of consciousness that you are 'unconscious' of.

Working tirelessly behind the scenes, your unconscious mind performs many remarkable tasks without you having to be aware of any of them happening. It manages your memories, creates your emotions, drives your behaviours and is instrumental in healing your body. Understanding how the unconscious mind works and, more specifically, how it impacts the degree to which you resist life and experience negative emotions, is vital when helping the body heal.

Uncovering the more subtle cause of resistance
Have you ever noticed how the exact same event can happen to two different people, whether that's giving a presentation or a flight being delayed, but how one person can get very upset and stressed whilst the other takes it in their stride? Different responses to the exact same events are possible because we all have a unique version of reality.

Your version of reality is the result of your unique unconscious filters.

It works like this: You gather information about your external environment via your five senses. At the point it reaches your brain and body it is raw data, without meaning - just light reflecting off the back of your eye to create pictures and vibration, making your inner eardrum move to produce sound.

Your unconscious mind then takes that raw data and makes meaning from the information by drawing on your internal filters, including, your language, beliefs, values, past decisions, memories, significant emotional events and a few more. This unconscious process deletes, distorts and generalizes the data to create your unique version of reality - unique because you have a unique set of internal filters. Helping your body heal by reducing stress therefore requires you to change any filters that are causing you to resist life events.

Discover the real Root-Cause Reason

By far the most impactful filter having the biggest impact on health is that of your beliefs because they silently work behind the scenes, justifying the emotions you feel as you encounter different life events. Beliefs exist in the more subtle unconscious realms of your mind, which can make them difficult to find and fix – unless you know how! To do exactly this, the Method you are about to learn in Part 2 first finds what I refer to as the Root-Cause Event (RCE).

This is the significant emotional event in your life when it is most likely that you created the Unhealthy Belief. Then, to discover what the Unhealthy Belief is, my method then goes on to find the Root-Cause Reason (RCR), which is a short sentence that includes the emotion(s) you felt at the time and the reasons why the Root-Cause Event made you feel that way. Make sense so far? OK, let's continue.

Discovering the Root-Cause Reason requires you to recognise that it's never what happened, but instead, *why* what happened was a problem for you, that is the *real* problem. In other words, it is the meaning you attached to what happened, the emotions you felt as a result, and the subsequent conclusions that you came to (or already had), that determines whether something is a problem for you, or not.

Therefore, the Root-Cause Reason, in most cases, is a short sentence that summarises in a few words *why* what happened was a problem from you; usually consisting of one or more negative emotions and the main reason you felt/feel that way. Examples include: "*Sad, scared and vulnerable when dad left*" or "*angry made to look stupid*" or "*rejected when mum preferred my brother*" or "*scared mum weak*" and so on.

The emotional domino effect
You cannot change what happened in your past, but you can change how you relate to what happened.

Therefore, to heal your past, you do NOT heal *what* happened, but instead, *why* what happened was a problem for you, namely, the Root-Cause Reason. Even better news is: if you focus on healing the Root-Cause Reasons justifying your Unhealthy Beliefs, you can heal multiple memories simultaneously.

By finding the theme that ties your problematic memories together you can heal a lifetime of emotional baggage in minutes!

Such a claim is possible due to the way the mind works. Your unconscious mind works behind the scenes helping you to recognise the people, places, events and things you encounter during your daily life. By asking, *"Where have I seen / heard / smelt / felt / tasted this before?"* and then searching your memories for similar experiences, it helps you make sense of whatever is happening each moment.

To make its job easier, your mind links similar memories together. It links memories about the same place or person together for instance. This is why when you hear a particular song it might remind you of a particular person, place or event and before you know it you can be taking a jaunt down memory lane. Or why it can be so emotionally difficult after a relationship break-up because everywhere you go can end up reminding you of the very person you're trying to forget!

The great news is that because your memories are linked together, you can benefit from what I call the *emotional domino effect*. By clearing the emotion associated with one key memory, (what I call the Root-Cause Event), you can clear the emotions from all associated memories too - simultaneously! Making it possible to clear a huge amount of emotional baggage in a very short amount of time!

The trick to the emotional domino effect is to find the common thread that ties your problematic past memories together.

Exploring the common themes

Explore what theme(s) link the majority of your 'bad' memories together. You can do the same with your life problems too. If you find the theme, in many cases, you will be well on your way to finding and healing the hidden Unhealthy Beliefs. For example, you may discover that you always tend to feel "lost" or "isolated" or "abandoned" or "not wanted" or "alone" or "not loved" or "a failure" or "let down" or "lonely" or "unprotected" etc. The theme often becomes an Unhealthy Belief – such as "I'm lost", "I'm not loved" etc. Therefore, you want to focus on healing the theme of being "lost" or "unloved" etc.

I've found repeatedly that by healing the reasons *why* your problems have existed, your problems have no alternative but to disappear for good. Imagine that!

PEACE FOR LIFE

SECRET #6
Unhealthy Beliefs can be easy to heal

The belief that it is hard to change Unhealthy Beliefs is a belief you can easily change!

Beliefs play a key role in determining the health of your body and the quality of your life. However, whenever I used to sit down with clients and tell them we were going to change one of their Unhealthy Beliefs it would be common to see the whites of their eyes due the myth that states it is hard to change beliefs. In my experience this simply isn't true. In reality we are forming new beliefs all of the time.

What's hiding in your closet?
I bet there is an item of clothing in your wardrobe that you bought a few years ago that, at the time, you *believed* made you look good. You strutted your stuff and felt fantastic wearing it! However, your tastes in clothing have changed so much that now someone would need to pay *you* to wear it! Fashion tastes changing is just one example of beliefs changing easily and naturally.

Desiring to help my clients more easily change their mind, I started referring to beliefs in a way that made them more palatable to change. These days I often call them conclusions.

Beliefs are nothing more than conclusions you've come to at some point in your life, based upon the limited information you had available at the time.

Making sense of the world you were born into, you came to conclusions about your personality (if you're outgoing or shy), your tastes (what you like or dislike), your capabilities (what you can and can't do), your self-worth, lovability and so on. Many of these conclusions serve you. (As I'd suggest you are doing a much better job *being you* than you may sometimes give yourself credit for!) However, some conclusions may be negatively impacting your health, wealth, relationships, career and life success. The good news is that if you have come to some unhelpful conclusions, there are 3 reasons why they can be easy to heal:

REASON # 1:
Beliefs are not absolutely true
Truth is always true. Beliefs are only sometimes correct, in some circumstances, for a select few, in limited locations, at certain times. Truths on the other hand are always true, in all circumstances, for everyone, in all time and space.

The good news is that <u>all</u> beliefs are only relatively true. Any conclusion you have, such as, 'it's hard to make money', may appear correct for you, but I can guarantee someone else on the planet believes the exact opposite. So which belief is true? Both! But it doesn't make either belief absolutely true, only relatively true. Get the difference? And because beliefs are only relatively true, they are not fixed. Beliefs can be changed... easily!

You are not a victim of your belief system.
You can change it if it isn't working for you and I'd
recommend you do if any of your beliefs are limiting
your health, wealth, peace, love and happiness.

REASON #2:
Beliefs are fuelled by feelings not facts
Consider this: How do you know something is true for you? Most people say, because a) it feels true, and b) because I have evidence to prove it to be true. And they'd be right, however, these criteria do not make their beliefs *absolutely* true.

One reason why people believe their beliefs for so long without questioning them is because they feel true. You have many thoughts passing through your mind everyday that do not limit your life or impact your body in any way. And you have thoughts that feel true to you. These are your beliefs. But guess what happens when you clear the emotions associated with the Unhealthy Beliefs? Yes, that's right, they immediately start to feel less true. And you stop believing them as much.

REASON #3:
Beliefs are based upon limited information
Amazingly, you came to most of the core beliefs
about yourself, other people and the world you live
in by the age of six, a sprinkling more by age 12 and
then only a few others since. Meaning you could
have beliefs affecting your health when you're 40 that
you came to when you were four! (Which is what I
find with many people I meet.)

The *younger you* came to these conclusions with very
little conscious awareness and life experience. No
wonder your Unhealthy Beliefs are rarely correct!
The good news is you naturally know much more
now than you did in the past. More importantly,
with new information you can come to new
conclusions any time you want. I mean it! (You will
find this out for yourself in Part 2)

SECRET #7
Being present helps the body to heal

*Thankfully, to enjoy more peace we don't need to
become time travellers able to change the past or
future. We just need to learn to be more present.*

So far you've discovered that to help your body heal
you need to stop resisting your life – past, present
and future. And you need to prioritise your peace by

letting go of anger, sadness, fear, guilt, grief, and anxiety along with any other downward spiralling emotional experiences.

Sound difficult? In reality, it need not be.

Freeing yourself from resistance and negative emotions can become much easier when you know and directly experience the benefits of this final secret, which incidentally, is perhaps one of the best-kept secrets in history. Namely, that *this* moment is the *only* moment that exists. And therefore, the only moment that is real. This one! No other. Not some past memory or future possibility, only now.

Unfortunately, millions of people live their entire lives not recognizing this simple truth. They go through their days going over their past or pre-playing future scenarios in their mind, again and again and again. Suffering from unnecessary stress, ill health and struggle in the process, simply because they are in their heads thinking about the past and future, missing the present moment.

Your body doesn't know the difference

Numerous scientific studies have now discovered that, biochemically speaking; your body cannot tell the difference between what is happening in the real world and what is imagined in your mind. Meaning that even if you are only *thinking* about a stressful situation, your body still experiences the same negative physical reactions as it would if these events were *actually* happening in reality. Quite remarkable, I'm sure you'll agree! The implications of these findings are hugely significant when it comes to your self-healing. Not only does it explain why so many people on the planet are experiencing physical conditions. It also validates the importance of learning how to think less and be more present.

The light relief from seeing the light

Words cannot describe the relief that came to me the day I discovered my memories from the past (irrespective of how bad or sad they were), are only accessible, now, via my imagination. And the same went for my future fears. For years I'd quite literally been scared by my shadow, my imagination. This made all therapy to change or let go of *my* problems so much easier now I knew the past was nothing more than an imagined story in my mind.

The product of my over-active imagination

When I was a child I snuck into the television room late one evening and watched the movie Jaws. It scared me to death! For weeks after seeing the movie I couldn't sleep. Convinced the big shark from the movie was hiding in my wardrobe, waiting for me to go to sleep before it came out to eat me! Now, looking back on it I can't help but laugh at the thought of a giant fish living in my wardrobe, but it felt so real at the time I would sweat and shake from fear. When my parents told me it wasn't real, it was just my imagination, I didn't believe them because it *felt* so real. But they spoke the truth and gave me one of the most important lessons of my life. I've now discovered that my problems exist mainly in my mind, in either my imagined past or future, but rarely, in the real world of *this* moment.

But what if much of the emotional stress negatively impacts your health and peace of mind is very similar? Although the problems may feel real, they exist more in your imagination than in reality?

Bitter pill?
Now I appreciate this might be a bit hard to swallow at first, especially if your problems feel real and appear to be happening now. But for the sake of your health, I invite you to notice that much of the stress and negative emotions you experience is caused by overly thinking about the past and future.

Meet Mandy, who had been emotionally taunted by past events for 22 years... "I came to Sandy's retreat having been troubled by negative emotions relating to three people for over 22 years. These memories had impacted my weight and I'd suffered from anger and depression. After my one-to-one with Sandy I felt unburdened, and completely relieved of all the pain I'd been carrying."

Mandy recognised during our meeting that the things she considered problems today were not problems in reality, but only stories in her mind. She let go of 22 years of pain in a matter of minutes when she realized she was causing herself unnecessary stress by continuing to think about what happened in her past. I showed her how to be more present and she recognized the difference between being present and being in her head thinking about the past. That gave her the choice of staying in the peace of the present moment or stepping into the pain of her past stories. It also stopped her being a victim to a past she couldn't change.

Perhaps ironically, we are going to explore being present in much greater details *later* in Part 3. But as a sneak preview, I invite you to start to notice that *this* moment, right now, is happening. You are reading this page and everything about *this* moment is actually OK. It might even be better than just OK! You may be clothed and fed, sitting comfortably and enjoying the experience of reading *this* word. Become super attentive to *this* moment and you can begin to notice there is a quiet peace that is inwardly present.

Being present is not only about noticing what's happening now. As you are going to discover, it's more about becoming aware of your presence, your being, your inner quietness, and your stillness. Because as you put your attention on *this* moment, you find you have to take your attention away from this moment, to start thinking about any problems.

Thinking is often an unconscious action, and it is a habit to put your attention on the past and future. But if you play with being super attentive to now, you will notice the dance that happens between *this* moment and your mind.

Move beyond problems, for good

By being present you can free yourself from harmful stress as you resist life less. You stop holding onto the past nor fighting what might happen in the future. The mind is the master and the body is the servant. The body follows the mind. The natural by-product of a peaceful mind is a resting body. A resting body is able to heal, as it naturally wants to. Enabling it to be in balance, function as it was meant to, age well and experience true vitality.

By letting go of the Unhealthy Beliefs and judgements held within your mind you can even experience life as if there is nothing wrong. Life is perfect. You are perfect. Life is complete. You are complete. Life isn't broken, and neither are you.

You rest in the knowledge that better health, peace of mind and happiness is your birthright, your most natural way of being. It comes to you when you stop resisting life and instead, focus your attention on enjoying the peace that naturally occurs when you are fully embracing the present moment you're in.

Summary of the 7 Self-Healing Secrets

SECRET #1
Your body *is* your mind
Evidence of the mind can be found throughout your entire body – making it scientifically accurate to say your body is a physical manifestation of your mind. As a result, your physical wellness is very much linked with your mental and emotional wellbeing.

SECRET #2
Your beliefs become your body
Beliefs impact how you relate to your life and therefore the stress you experience. Your beliefs also determine the messages sent between the mind and the body, which in turn can impact upon the body's physical functioning.

SECRET #3
Your body is not against you
Symptoms many consider to be physical problems are often your body's best attempt at adapting to survive. By changing how you perceive life, your body can adapt again, but this time by functioning in a more desirable way.

SECRET #4
Regular resistance is bad for your health
Chronic stress, caused by chronic resistance, is a major cause of problems. By learning to resist life less, your body has more opportunities to heal.

SECRET #5
Cure the hidden Root-Cause Reasons
By changing your unconscious Unhealthy Beliefs you can help the body heal, let go of stored emotional baggage, change unhelpful behaviours, and enjoy enhanced wellbeing.

SECRET #6
Unhealthy Beliefs can be easy to heal
It is a myth that beliefs are hard to heal. Beliefs can be changed because they are never absolutely true, are fuelled by feelings not facts and are based upon limited (often wrong) information. With new insight you can come to new conclusions anytime you want.

SECRET #7
Being present helps the body to heal
Much physical stress comes from thinking about the past and future. To be present is to be beyond your mind, resting in the still conscious awareness that is your Real Self (more about this in Part 3). When the mind rests, the body heals. Naturally, you enjoy better health, peace of mind and happiness.

Now that you know my self-healing secrets you are ready to experience the method for yourself. It's time to discover any hidden Unhealthy Beliefs that may be negatively impacting your health and happiness, so you can be free from them, for good!

PEACE FOR LIFE

PART TWO

peace
with your
past

I highly recommend you...

Prepare properly

Read chapters 4, 5 and 6 before attempting to use my method on any problem. Please do not use this method on your own without the guidance of a trained Mind Detox Practitioner if you believe there is a chance you could find a past event that you would not want to work on by yourself. If in doubt, please see the Clinics area of my website (www.minddetox.com) to find a trained and qualified Practitioner near you.

No problem?

If you have no physical, emotional and life problems right now, then read through the list of 20 Unhealthy Beliefs in Appendix 2 (page 193) to check you don't have any beliefs that could cause you problems in the future. If none of these Unhealthy Beliefs feel true, then great! Go straight to Part 3 to explore even more ways to enjoy peace for life.

CHAPTER FOUR
Discover your unhealthy beliefs

Virtually every aspect of your daily life is impacted by your current beliefs. Unhealthy Beliefs have the power to impact on your body (due to the mind-body connection), your emotions (because they impact on how you interpret life), and your life circumstance (because your beliefs determine your choices and actions). Therefore, by healing your Unhealthy Beliefs it is possible to cause positive changes to occur within your body, your emotions and your life.

Despite this, many people find it hard to change their Unhealthy Beliefs because they don't know what they are, don't know how to find them or don't know how to change them. Fortunately, for you, this is exactly what my 5-Step Method does!

Summary of 5-Step Method

My method heals the hidden Unhealthy Beliefs that may be causing your current problems. To find the beliefs, we access them via a past significant emotional event (when you most likely formed the belief). To do this, choose a current problem you want to heal and follow these 5 steps:

STEP 1: **WHEN IT STARTED?**
Finds the age of the Root-Cause Event.

STEP 2: **WHAT HAPPENED?**
Helps you to recall the memory of what happened.

STEP 3: **WHY WAS IT A PROBLEM?**
Explores why what happened was a problem for you so you can define the Root-Cause Reason.

STEP 4: **WHY NOT A PROBLEM NOW?**
Considers what you know now that can help you be at peace with the past.

STEP 5: **TEST THE WORK**
Checks the emotional rating for how the memory feels when you think about it now. If the memory feels neutral, then the Unhealthy Belief is healed.

Key of important terms used in the next pages:

Root-Cause Event
This is the significant emotional event in your past.

Root-Cause Conclusion
This is the conclusion you came to as a result of the Root-Cause Event happening.

Root-Cause Reason
This is the reason why the Root-Cause Event was a problem for you. It is a short sentence with an emotional element and the main reason(s) why you felt the way you did.

Unhealthy Belief
This is the same as the Root-Cause Conclusion. I used the name 'beliefs' because readers are more familiar with the term. You will discover that all Unhealthy Beliefs stem from one or more corresponding Root-Cause Reason(s).

STEP #1
WHEN IT STARTED?
(Find Root-Cause Event)

Choose the physical condition, emotional issue or life problem that you would like to heal. With your permission, let's find out when this problem started so that you can move on and stop it being a problem now. Trust your first answer to all of the following questions:

ASK: What event in my life is the cause of (state problem here), the first event which when resolved will cause the problem to disappear? If I were to know, what age was I?

(For example, "what event in my life is the cause of the psoriasis / anxiety / depression / migraines / (whatever the problem is), the first event which when resolved...")

TOP TIP
Avoid editing your thoughts or disregarding your immediate answer if it is not what you expected. In most cases, the Root-Cause Event happened before the age of 10 so by trusting your first answer you can more easily discover the right Root-Cause Event.

From a sea of infinite possibilities, the answer to this question gives you a specific moment in time, (age 2, 6 or 16 for instance). This helps your mind remember the memory of the possible Root-Cause Event now. Once you have an age, it's time to move onto...

STEP #2
WHAT HAPPENED?
(Clarify the Context)

Let's find out more information about what happened at that age so you can establish the Root-Cause Event that was a problem for you. You will do this by clarifying the context: the specific person(s), place, event(s) or thing(s) that were involved. Hold the age (you found in Step 1) in your mind whilst you trust your first answers to the following question:

ASK: When I think of that time, what is the first person, place, event or thing to come to mind now?

Examples of possible answers include:
*The first **person** might be: "dad" or "mum" or "grandfather" or "school teacher" or "brother" or "best friend" etc.*

*The first **place** might be: "home" or "kitchen" or "bedroom" or "the park near my house" or "nursery/school" and so on.*

*The first **event** might be: "an argument" or "first day of school" or "getting lost" or "being shouted at" or "someone leaving" or "getting answer wrong" etc.*

*The first **thing** might be: "my teddy" or "grandmother's perfume" or "being cold" or "being scared" or "box of matches" or anything that is symbolic that your mind is giving you to help you remember the entire memory.*

Remembering the memory now

A specific detailed memory might have been recalled by now. If not, then you want to remain open-minded and curious about what might have happened around that time in your life. It can feel like you are making it up, that's normal. You may need to dig around a bit before the complete memory returns to your conscious awareness. In the same way a detective or an interested friend would ask questions to find out what happened, you might want to also ask:

When I think of this (state person, place, etc.), what else comes to mind? Who was there? Where was I? What might have happened in relation to (state person, place, etc.) around that time in my life?

For example, if your answer to step 1 was "age 4" and your first answer to step 2 was "dad" then ask, *"When I think about age 4 and my dad, what else comes to mind?"* Or, if your first answer had been "box of matches" then ask: *"When I think of age 4 and a box of matches, who or where pops into my mind now?"* Who else might have been there? What else was going on?

Like an artist painting a picture, aim to gather as many details as you need to paint an accurate picture of what might have happened. Your goal is to find a memory of an event that could have been a problem for you then. The moment you find a problematic memory immediately go to STEP 3 (page 78).

Struggling to find a memory? ASK:

✓ *When in my life did I not have this problem?*
✓ *When did I first notice I had this problem?*
✓ *How long have I had this problem?*
✓ *What was happening the 12 to 18 month leading up to the first time I noticed the problem?*

These questions can give you clues as to the possible Root-Cause Event. For instance, I once asked a client who'd been suffering from migraines, *"when did you first notice you had migraines?"* She remembered that she'd got her first migraine around the time a friend committed suicide. This then reminded her of a younger memory, aged 12, when her aunt died suddenly. We worked on healing the age-12 memory (which when we did, she stopped getting migraines).

Still not found a memory? Don't worry, try this:
Create an emotional events tracker. In a journal, write down, in age order, all the significant emotional events of your life thus far. For example:

Age 4: Scared leaving mum at the school gates.
Age 7: Sad when best friend moved away.
Age 8: Scared when lost at the supermarket.
Age 12: Hurt not invited to friend's party.
And so on.

Keep exploring what might have happened until you find a specific event that could have been a problem for you. If you find this impossible, then work on a more recent memory that you can remember that comes to mind when you think about the physical condition, emotional issue or life problems. Once you have found a problematic memory, you are ready to progress on to...

STEP #3
WHY WAS IT A PROBLEM?
(Find the Root-Cause Reason)

Unless you have a time machine of sorts, you cannot change what has happened in your past. However, the great news is you don't have to. You can change your relationship *with* what happened. To do this we don't work on *what* happened, but instead, we focus on *why* what happened was a problem for you, then. This is a much more effective way to heal past memories because when you heal the reason *why* it was a problem, then there is no reason for it be a problem anymore.

Find the Root-Cause Reason
The Root-Cause Reason (RCR) is the reason why what happened was a problem for you. To discover it you explore how you interpreted the past events, the subsequent emotions you felt, and the possible conclusions you came to in light of the significant emotional events that happened.

Bring to mind the Root-Cause Event you discovered in Steps 1 and 2, so you can now discover the RCR:

FOR EMOTIONS ASK:
What is it about what happened that was a problem for me? How did it make me feel?

Ask yourself the above questions until you get one or more negative emotions. Then ask yourself:

FOR REASONS ASK:
Ultimately, what was it about what happened that caused me to feel that way?

Keep it simple: Don't over complicate this part of the method. You simply want to consider why you felt the way you did. So you can find the *biggest reason* for feeling bad at that moment in your life. Aim to state the Root-Cause Reason in uncomplicated simple words.

Remember you probably came to the conclusion when you were very young. It can help to include the emotions in the answer to your question by saying:

Ultimately, I felt (sad or scared or angry etc) because... (Say the first reason that comes to mind.)

Once you have emotion(s) and the reason(s) you are ready to put them together to create the Root-Cause Reason for the problem you want to heal:

Root-Cause Reason Statement
= Emotion(s)   +   Reason(s)
   (What you felt)   (Why you felt that way)

(Examples include: "Sad, scared and vulnerable dad disappeared" or "angry forced to move house" or "scared mum so weak" etc. I have shared approximately 300 real-life Root-Cause Reasons in Appendix 2 to help you fully understand what you are looking for here.)

When you find a Root-Cause Reason, rate it:

ASK: On a scale of 0 to 10, with 10 being very high emotion and feels true, how would I rate (state Root-Cause Reason)?

Root-Cause Reasons that have the power to justify an Unhealthy Belief or cause a physical condition or life problem usually have the emotional intensity of 8, 9 or 10 out of 10 (with 10 being very high emotion). If your RCR scores 7 or less then you might want to further explore the reasons why what happened was a problem for you or see if there is a more emotionally significant Root-Cause Event to work on.

∞

QUICK TIME-OUT TO CHECK-IN

By this point in the method you should have discovered a Root-Cause Reason; which is a short sentence that summaries why the Root-Cause Event was a problem for you then.

Don't forget, while this sentence may feel true, that does not make it absolutely true. If you have found an emotionally charged Root-Cause Reason then I suggest you immediately go to Chapter 5 to heal it.

Not found a Root-Cause Reason? Don't worry!
Turn to Appendix 2 (page 193) now where you will find I've done all the hard work for you. As I reveal the 20 most common Unhealthy Beliefs and their associated real-life Root-Cause Reasons.

CHAPTER FIVE
Heal your unhealthy beliefs

Pay close attention! This is a very important moment in your life. Now that you've discovered the Root-Cause Reason(s) that have been justifying one or more Unhealthy Belief(s), I highly recommended you immediately move on to heal what you've found.

The purpose of Step 4 of the Method is to heal any Root-Cause Reasons that might be justifying the existence of Unhealthy Beliefs. Remember, problems are only problems today because of the incorrect conclusions you've come to in the past. And the even better news is your Unhealthy Beliefs are easy to heal because:

REASON # 1
Beliefs are not absolutely true
Truth is always true. Beliefs are only sometimes correct. Therefore, beliefs can be updated.

REASON #2
Beliefs are fuelled by feelings not facts
The 'realness' of beliefs is based largely on them feeling true, but just because something feels true doesn't make it truth. Clearing the emotions makes them feel less true for you.

REASON #3
Beliefs are based upon limited information
You now know more than you did in the past. With the benefit of hindsight you can think about old events from a more peaceful and compassionate perspective. With new information you can come to new conclusions anytime you want.

It's never too late to have a happy childhood
You are now going to come to some new, healthier, conclusions about the Root-Cause Event and, in the process, let go of any emotions associated with the Root-Cause Reason(s). The goal of this step of the method is to be able to think about the past event and Root-Cause Reason and feel totally neutral.

To be able to feel at peace when thinking about events that used to cause you negative emotions is evidence that any Unhealthy Belief(s) stemming from the event have been healed. You quite literally no longer believe it is justified to feel bad about what happened. You've evolved beyond it being a problem for you. (Give yourself a pat on the back in advance because you are doing great work!)

Coming to more compassionate conclusions about past events can allow balance to be naturally restored in your body because the reason(s) for the imbalance have been removed.

Your body knows how to heal itself
Becoming aware of your Unhealthy Beliefs is the hardest part of the healing process. From now on, your healing journey gets easier. It is the job of your infinitely powerful inner intelligence to take care of the (healing) details. Your job is to let yourself be at peace with your past, (which is easier and less stressful than resisting what happened), so that your mind can give your body the green light for healing to take place.

Remember, changing your mind can cause changes to occur within the body due to the mind-body connection. You may even find that your inner pharmacy immediately gets to work healing any physical conditions the moment new messages start getting sent between your mind and body. Sound good? Great, now keep up the brilliant work you've started by moving onto...

STEP #4
WHY NOT A PROBLEM NOW?
(New conclusions with new information)

Hold the Root-Cause Event in your mind as you answer the following question:

What can I know now, that if I had known it in the past, I would have never felt (state Root-Cause Reason) in the first place?

You may need to ask yourself this question a few times to explore positive and loving learning. You are looking to find an alternative ways of thinking about the old event that would make it impossible to feel bad about what happened. (By this, I'm not saying your goal is to be happy that the bad thing happened, only neutral.) You will know you've found it because you will feel a sense of relief.

Other questions you can ask to explore positive and loving ways of thinking about past events include:

What do I need to know or learn, the knowing or learning of which will allow me to be at peace with what happened?

Is it possible for me to be at peace when I think about this event at some point in my life? OK, what could I know at that point in the future so that I could feel at peace then?

For this to have been a problem then, what did I need to not know? Or, for this to be a problem then, what was I pretending not to know?

If a friend had this problem, what advice would I give them to help them be more at peace with what happened?

For me to be at peace with this memory, once and for all, what do I need to say now?

The moment you find a positive and loving learning that makes peace with the original event and disproves the Unhealthy Belief, Install the Knowing.

ACTIVITY
Install the Knowing

Timing is everything when *installing the knowing*. It is to be done immediately when you discover the learning you need, such that if you had known it in the past, it would be *impossible* for you to have any negative emotions associated with what happened.

It works because any justifications you had to feel bad about the Root-Cause Event are undermined, stop feeling 'true', and you no longer have any justifiable reason to continue feeling bad. You are quite literally taking the new found positive and loving learning and installing it in your body-mind. It is powerful and when used correctly can be very quick and highly effective at completely clearing all negative emotions associated with the Root-Cause Event, Root-Cause Reason, and immediately heal the Unhealthy Belief.

Steps to Install the Knowing

Get positive and loving learning using Step 4 then:

STEP 1: ASK: *Where do I know this in my body?* (Notice where within your own heart, chest, solar plexus and stomach this knowing is in your body.)

STEP 2: ASK: *If the knowing had a colour, what colour would it be?* (Any colour will do so trust your first answer.)

STEP 3: Keep that knowing there now and close your eyes. Then use your imagination to go to the past, with that knowing, and play the movie of the old memory from beginning to end, but this time, with the knowing (state learning) and the colour (state location).

STEP 4: Come back to now by opening your eyes. This exercise should take about 30 seconds.

TOP TIP
If the Root-Cause Event is traumatic and you don't want to imagine it happening again, then once you notice where you know the knowing in your body, progress on to use Emotional Freedom Technique to clear the emotions and install the positive learning. See Appendix 3 (page 218) for full instructions.

Immediately after you have installed the knowing
Open your eyes and take your attention away from the problem and memory for a moment by distracting yourself. Look at a picture on the wall, notice something you can hear nearby, or sing a few seconds of a song that lifts your spirits. Do whatever it takes to temporarily take your attention away from what you've been working on. Then, once you've done that, you are ready to move on to the final step of the Method...

STEP #5
Test the work
Explore how emotionally neutral you feel now:

TEST THE PAST: *"On a scale of 10 to 0, with 0 being the emotion is completely gone now and I feel neutral, how would I rate the Root-Cause Event?*

(You might find the memory is there but the old emotion is gone and you feel more neutral now.)

TEST ROOT-CAUSE REASON: *"On a scale of 10 to 0, with 0 being the emotion is completely gone now and I feel neutral, how would I rate the old Root-Cause Reason?"*

TEST THE FUTURE *"Think of a time in the future when something like this could happen, but this time, notice how differently I respond, OK?"*

If the answers to the above questions are all 0/10 and you feel neutral, then great. Well done for all the great work you've done and congratulations!

All in one place

I'm aware the 5-Step Method has been taught over several pages. Personally, I find it easier if the main questions are all in one place. So I've put an *at a glance* summary of the 5-Step Method in Appendix 1 (page 189) for quick reference and ease of use. I've also provided a D.I.Y. Mind Detox Tool in Appendix 3 (page 223) for you to use too.

Still feeling something? Don't fret!

If you still feel any negative emotions relating to the Root-Cause Event or Root-Cause Reason, then it means there is a part of your mind that still feels justified to feel bad. This is a blind spot. So you need to turn to Chapter 6 now to explore my very powerful blind spot busting breakthroughs...

CHAPTER SIX
Blind spot busting breakthroughs

Struggling to clear any negative emotions or come to healthier conclusions? Relax! The following insights are great at healing the more stubborn Unhealthy Beliefs and emotional events.

Negative emotions exist for a reason. If you have any residual negative feelings about the Root-Cause Event or Root-Cause Reason then it just means you have a temporary '**blind spot**' in your mind. Blind spots are hidden justifications for feeling the way you feel. As long as you have the blind spot, your mind will not let go of *all* of the negative emotions because it will still believe it is justified to feel some anger, sadness, fear or whatever.

Shining a light on the blind spot is as simple as exploring more positive and loving ways of re-remembering the past. When you come to a new conclusion you will naturally feel better because there will be no reason to feel bad anymore. It just makes sense.

TOP TIP
Avoid the common trap

My method is entirely focused on healing the mind-based root-causes of problems, rather than treating the surface-level-symptoms. Negative emotions are caused by your Unhealthy Beliefs because it is your beliefs that determine how you feel in relation to what happens in your life. Therefore negative emotions are still only symptoms, not *the* cause.

Make sure when you're doing this work that you do not fall into the common trap of focusing all of your energy on trying to get rid of the negative emotions. They will naturally go when feeling bad is no longer justified. We only use the emotions as a useful gauge to determine whether or not you've come to new conclusions yet and have healed the belief.

(HINT: No Negative Emotion = No Unhealthy Belief)

10 blind spot busting breakthroughs

Having worked with literally hundreds of people, I've been privileged to be present when they've been resolving their biggest life problems by having their biggest life breakthroughs. Here are 10 of my favourite blind spot busting insights that repeatedly help people to come to more positive and loving conclusions. These blind spot busters are designed to help you question the assumptions you've been unconsciously making about past events or people. So only keep reading if you're willing to change your opinion about your past and the people in your life!

*(It is recommended that if any of these insights resonate with you to the point that you know it would be impossible to feel bad about the past problem, please immediately use the **Install the Knowing exercise** with that insight.)*

BLINDSPOT #1
I survived!

Fear can be hard to clear if your mind believes *staying scared* is keeping you safe. It isn't! Prolonged fear is harmful to your health. To put your mind at rest, I would like to highlight one very reassuring fact: for you to be reading this book it means you survived the significant emotional event(s). Obvious perhaps, but for many people it is a huge *a-ha* moment they had never considered before.

Consider this: *If you had known, for absolute certain, that you were going to survive the past event, how differently would you have felt at the time?* You might find that you could have experienced the event, but would have been more calm in the knowledge you were going to be OK.

Instead of focusing on how scared or vulnerable you may have felt, start to appreciate how resourceful and resilient you *actually* are. After all, you survived! In acknowledging you survived, you naturally give your mind permission to let go of feelings of hurt, anger, sadness or fear, to be replaced with calmness and the knowledge that everything is going to be OK.

BLINDSPOT #2
I was forgetting what happened next

Leading on from blind spot 1, cast your mind back to a point **after** the Root-Cause Event when you knew for certain that you were safe and were going to be OK. Although it is natural for the mind to be drawn to think about the most traumatic parts of the past, it is very healing to acknowledge that, although it was traumatic then, you've now ended up safe.

The dreamer
A good friend of mine had been experiencing intense dreams that would cause him to lash out during

sleep. When I asked him the questions from the method, he said he remembered his Dad and how angry he was. I then simply asked him *"what happened next?"* And he immediately burst out laughing and said, *"well, nothing!!!"* He reported having more deep and peaceful sleep from then on. I believe my friend realising this allowed his mind to switch off 'high alert mode' and let him enter and enjoy deeper levels of sleep.

But what if something bad *did* happen next?
I can almost guarantee that there has been a point since the traumatic time that you have become safe again. (Even if that time is right now as you read this page!) Explore focusing more on how safe and well you are *now* rather than how you *were* in the past. Doing so can help your body-mind disengage panic mode and heal more effectively.

BLINDSPOT #3
I was doing my best and so were they

Inside every human heart is the desire to be happy and to experience love. I've asked literally hundreds of people what they want more than anything else in life. I've asked people with different financial backgrounds, religious preferences, ages and educations. Of these people, how many of them do you think told me they wanted conflict, separation, anger, arguments, or anything else negative? That's right, zero. Nobody. Nada! Every single person I've asked has wanted positive life experiences, such as peace, happiness, health and love.

Everyone wants peace, including the people who do horrible things.

Blinded by their misinformed mind
If given a *genuine* choice (i.e. if they were not being blinded by their own Unhealthy Beliefs), I believe anyone who has *wronged you* would always choose options that would move them towards greater happiness, peace and love – if they knew how.

People who don't know how to be at peace, enjoy happiness, or experience love, don't need your criticism or anger, they need your compassion. You do not need to agree with their actions, only understand they were doing their best, given their own Unhealthy Beliefs. Remembering this can help you see yourself and others from a more gentle, understanding and compassionate perspective.

Are you simply being too hard on yourself?
Have your forgotten that you sometimes have to make mistakes in order to learn what is right? Are you ignoring that you were young, innocent, doing your best, and, at that point, didn't know any different?

For residual guilt, remember that at the time in your life you did what you did, you would not have done it unless you *believed* it was the best possible option available, given your set of circumstances at that time. There's no point looking back now, from a completely different time and set of circumstances, to judge or feel guilty about what you did in the past. You've had many life experiences that have shaped you since and would cause you to act differently in similar circumstances today. (Even reading this book makes you a different person to who you were then!) Let learning from it be enough and let go of any guilt.

BLINDSPOT #4
They had their own issues to deal with

This insight is especially relevant if you felt neglected or let down by your parents when growing up.

As young children we see our parents as Gods. They knew everything, were all-powerful, had no problems, and could do absolutely anything. It is only as we grew up to become adults ourselves that we began to appreciate that they were *only* human and probably had their own difficulties, fears, emotional baggage and stress to deal with. Furthermore, and at the risk of sounding crude, allow me to highlight an important point. Your parents had sex (or *made love* if you prefer), and created a baby. In the moment of conception, they didn't suddenly heal all of their 'issues' or become enlightened. They *only* became parents. Let's give them a break.

> *They shouldn't have known better because they couldn't have known better.*

By taking into consideration the challenging lives our parents (or other people) had, it can become easier to understand why they left, or why they were moody sometimes, or why they found it hard to love us fully.

Quite remarkably, by acknowledging other people have their own issues to deal with something magical happens - *you* stop taking how they were towards you so personally. This enables you to let go of any hurt, sadness, anger, guilt or feelings of being unloved or unwanted etc. and move on viewing them from a more understanding and loving perspective.

BLINDSPOT #5
It wasn't personal

One of the most common reasons people hold onto negative emotions for years is because they believe the actions of other people have something to do with them. They don't!

Everyone has a unique version of reality. Remember it works like this: People gather information about their external environment via the five senses. At the point it reaches the mind and nervous system it is raw data, without meaning, just light reflecting off the back of the eye to create pictures and vibration making the inner eardrum move to produce sound. The unconscious mind then takes that raw data and makes meaning from it by drawing on a unique set of filters, including, beliefs, values, past decisions, memories, significant emotional events and so on. This process deletes, distorts and generalizes the data received to create a unique internal version of life.

Meaning not only do you see, hear and experience a massively edited version of reality. Everyone else on this planet does too!

Due to everyone having a unique version of reality (unless a person is enlightened and can see beyond their beliefs), most people end up projecting out into the world their conditioning. This causes other people to not necessarily see, hear or experience the REAL you, but only their IDEA of you, based upon *their* internal filters. Get the difference?

Believe it or not this is great news when it comes to you being able to get peace with your past. It means that YOU have never (and I mean never) been left, rejected, hated or abandoned by anyone in your past. What your parents or peers or partners have not liked or rejected has only ever been THEIR IDEAS about you, which was not YOU - just their idea, in their mind, based upon their conditioned beliefs, values, memories, significant emotional events etc. Your mum did not prefer your brother or sister; she only preferred the idea she had in her head about your sibling. Your Dad didn't leave you; he left his idea of you, based upon his own issues, conditioning and Unhealthy Beliefs. Your ex didn't fall out of love with you. He or she came to dislike their *idea* of you, which was and is not you.

Only an idea! It wasn't personal. What a relief.

∞

A QUICK TIME-OUT TO CHECK- IN

Now that we are half way through the blind spot busting breakthroughs, it seems like the perfect moment to take a quick time-out to explore an intriguing observation that can help to undermine the validity of any problem you may be looking to heal.

Here one minute, gone the next

Amongst other adventures, a large part of my life involves travelling the world helping people get peace with the past. For some, they've been experiencing extreme anger or sadness or fear for decades. For others, they've resisted life so much and for so long they've ended up with severe physical conditions. Yet, irrespective of how long difficult event(s) have been a problem for them, there is always a point when they discover a way of thinking about the past that stops it being a problem. In doing so, they end up feeling more neutral or even positive towards life events that, for years, had been causing them intense negative feelings.

Witnessing this in literally hundreds of people led me to begin to question *what* problems actually are. I mean, if something is a problem for a person for years, and then, after a simple shift in viewpoint, stops being a problem, was it ever a problem in the first place? Or was the *real* problem the person not being able to view the life event(s) from a more positive and conscious perspective, yet?

Stepping beyond conditioned thinking

One of my favourite quotes by Einstein is: *"No problem can be solved with the same level of consciousness that created it"*. I've observed that it is people's open-mindedness and consciousness that determines whether what happens in life is a problem for them, or not. Not the event, but what they think about the event. One person can lose their job and be thrilled at the adventure, another can become physically ill from the stress. What's the difference? The life event is the same, but their perceptions of it are different.

Raising your consciousness to ever-increasing heights by bursting through your blind spots is a marvellous thing to do. It can lead you into the direct experience of a life lived free from problems. Whereby, although unexpected challenges may still arise, you don't experience them as being problems, nor as anything being wrong. How incredible is that? You don't need to wait for anything to change about your past, present, or future, for you to experience inner peace. When you change your mind, everything changes!

Remember, you are not trying to get over problematic life events, but rather, you are getting over your conditioned thinking about what's happened.

Enjoying peace for life becomes easier from this fresh perspective, so let's get back to exploring more blind spot busting breakthroughs:

BLINDSPOT #6
I've been mind reading

Have you ever been mean to someone you love? Have you ever even told someone you love that you hate them? Or ever pushed them away? Or not been there for them when they might have needed you? If you've answered 'yes' to any of these questions, then how can you know for certain that if someone shouted at you or was mean to you or wasn't there for you, that it automatically meant they didn't love you? That's right, you can't.

One of the most common Unhealthy Beliefs that cause physical conditions, emotional issues and life problems is the belief *'my parents didn't love me enough'*. In almost all cases, the belief is based upon a mind read. By that I mean the person had been reading between the lines, assumed they knew what other people were thinking and concluded the worst.

Then, in a total turnaround in thinking, most people I work with end up realising that they were in fact loved, very much indeed. In countless cases they recognise the parent (or whoever) simply didn't know *how* to express love in a way that made them feel loved. Which, I'm sure you will agree, is something completely different to *not* being loved! For instance, if a child is left by a parent, it is common for the child to come to the conclusion that it meant they were not loved or loveable. This simply is not the case. Coming to that conclusion is an assumption that is made based upon a mind-read.

Irrespective of the actions of another, you can never know for 100% certain what is really going on inside another person's mind.

In reality, most people you meet don't even know what's going on in their *own* mind! They are unconsciously acting out their conditioning. So how are *you* supposed to accurately predict *their* thoughts? You're not - so I highly recommend you don't waste your time trying. (And catch yourself when you do.)

All you need to know is this: It wasn't personal and the actions of other people have absolutely no relation to your lovability <u>whatsoever</u>.

Recognizing that a belief or Root-Cause Reason is based upon mind-read assumptions can undermine its correctness, and often causes negative emotions associated with the past to no longer be justified.

BLINDSPOT #7
It's OK for me to be happy

Losing someone you love can often cause feelings of grief. For many, it is a completely natural response. However, if the grief continues too long it can become harmful for the body and limit the vitality and life of the person still living.

People can get stuck in the cycle of grief if they maintain a connection with the person who's died by holding onto the grief, such that if they felt better it would somehow lose or dishonour the person who died. An important question to ask yourself if you're experiencing grief is: *Would my loved one want me to feel sad or experience any other negative emotion because of their death?* You can honour them by loving them whilst being at peace - like they want you to be now.

BLINDSPOT #8
I'm now able to look after myself

When you were first born you needed your parents completely - to feed you, clean you and protect you. Despite needing your parents when you were very young, you are now at a stage in life when you can feed, clean and look after yourself. Obvious things to say, perhaps, but for many it is a blind spot. Lots of people continue to hold onto negative emotions towards their parents for *not being there for them* when they were children. They continue to hold onto the anger, sadness, hurt or fear the child felt – as if they *still* depend on their parents for their survival.

Now I appreciate that it might have been justifiable to feel these feelings as a child, but as an adult, the emotions are way past their 'use by' date!

Waiting for a past that never comes

Subtle on-going resistance about how your parents were *in the past* can be destructive to your health, happiness and overall life success today. The resistance is caused by a blind spot in your mind that is *still* looking to get something from your parents, even if you don't actually need it anymore.

Take a moment to fully acknowledge that you are all grown up now. You are able to clothe, feed and look

after yourself (even if you don't want to!). You can b
safe and survive very well on your own.

Repeat after me... *"I can look after myself, I don't nee
my parents anymore and even though I might nc
necessarily agree with how they raised me, whatever the
did worked well at teaching me how to look after myself, b
safe and resourceful in this world. Good job parents!"*

BLINDSPOT #9
Compassion sets me free

Compassion is a combination of unconditional lov
and wisdom. It is the ability and willingness to lov
others exactly as they are, in the knowledge tha
every person on the planet is doing the best they car
and wants to experience peace of mind and love.

Being compassionate means if someone else is havin;
a hard time or being difficult, you don't join them b
feeling bad too. Instead, you stay peaceful withi
your Real Self (more about this in Part 3), and shov
them ways to get out of the hole they're in.

Although not feeling bad might sound a bit uncarin;
at first, it is the only way to truly help others. If yo
always agree with the other person that they ar
broken or get upset with them, you will onl
reinforce their justifications for being in the hole

which keeps them feeling bad even longer. I'm sure you don't want that for them, or yourself.

Imagine a friend calls you, upset because they've split up with yet another partner. They tell you, *"all men are bastards, let's go out and get drunk!!!"* Compassion wouldn't necessarily agree with them because it might not be useful for them to go-on believing that. If this person keeps creating bad relationships, it is more useful to help them see why it's happening and what they can do to enjoy more loving relationships.

Much better to compassionately say what you see, rather than blindly agree with your friend, talk about your failed relationships all night over too much wine and end up with a hangover the next day. (And perhaps even the start of yet another doomed relationship!)

On a more serious note, what if you were abused or attacked? Compassion works in a similar way. Although difficult experiences like these often lead to feelings of hurt, sadness or fear. Compassion can set you free from toxic emotions like these too.

Rather than getting angry or upset about what someone did, for the sake of your own peace and wellbeing, be willing to view them from a more compassionate perspective. They, like you, want to be happy and know they are loved. Every human, without exception, ultimately wants that as the desire is built in from birth. However, at that time in their lives they didn't know how.

Maybe they had difficult upbringings without any positive role models so didn't know how to treat you lovingly? Maybe they didn't love themselves fully so projected judgments out onto you? Or perhaps they were so critical of you because they wanted to make sure you had the opportunities they didn't? Who knows? Don't try to figure it out because it would only be a mind read. Instead, play with seeing the problematic person through more compassionate eyes; you will be amazed at how free you can be.

BLINDSPOT #10
I wasn't being very loving either

Some people hold onto rejection or resentment for years because someone didn't love them in the way they believe they should be loved. Feeling fully justified in staying a victim to the other person not loving them enough, not being there for them, not being the parent they'd hoped for, and so on.

They almost fall off their chair when I ask them:

> *How good were you at loving your parent (or whoever) unconditionally?*

We then explore: *Is it possible you were waiting to be loved unconditionally, when at the same time, you were not loving the other person unconditionally? Did you constantly want the other person to change? Do you want the people in your life to change? Are you imposing your beliefs on the other person? What happens if, right now, you let the other person be enough, exactly as they are?* Don't worry, you don't have to love their actions, but for your own sake, let yourself love their heart.

What would Love do?

Another powerful question you can ask if you ever have a problem with a particular person is *'what would Love do now?"* Doing so often causes feelings of anger or resentment to fall away and be replaced with gentleness. Love is unconditional, non-judgemental, gives freely and needs absolutely nothing in return.

Remember, you experience love when you *give* love. Due to this wonderful truth, there is quite literally no limit on the amount of love you can enjoy during your days. Don't wait for someone else to love you before you love them. You might be the very person in their life to show *them* how to love more unconditionally. Be the light that guides others home to the heart.

PEACE FOR LIFE

PART THREE

enjoying
peace
for life

Welcome to part three of Peace for Life...

Freedom from physical conditions and emotional issues is marvellous, but even that can pale into insignificance compared to the freedom that can be experienced if you apply what you are about to learn in Part 3.

In my experience, cultivating a consistent sense of contentment, love, inner peace and joy during daily life requires you to focus less on *changing your mind,* and much more on *changing your relationship with your mind,* so that you can learn to rest in the heart of what I call your Real Self.

Part 3 comes from a different place to the rest of the book. You may find it even feels different to read. We focus less on changing and improving. More on loving what is, and letting each moment be enough. Because I want you to rediscover and reconnect with the peace that's always present.

CHAPTER SEVEN
The peace that's always present

Permanent peace is possible. Irrespective of what's happened during your life and who you think you are today, what you consider to be your successes and failures, good attributes and bad bits, your good deeds and downright awful ones and your ups and downs. Whether you have the body, looks, love life, education, career, money, home, hobbies or life you think you should. I'm here to tell you one indisputable truth.

None of these things ultimately matter. Not one iota. Not when it comes to you having the same ability as anyone else to experience peace of mind now. Yes you read that right; there are no pre-requisites, no rights of passage and nothing about you needs to change or improve, for you to enjoy peace for life.

You see, the truth is that whether you believe it or not, you are *already* an absolutely amazing, infinitely conscious, utterly gorgeous, perfectly peaceful, love filled human being. This is *what* you are. Whether you like it or not! All these wonderful things come built-in; your gift for being born. And it's your birthright to experience the *truth of what you are*.

You may not believe it. You may not feel it. It may not be your current experience. The truth is it doesn't stop it being true! Truth overrules beliefs and feelings. Truth is absolutely real and permanent. Beliefs and feelings are only relatively real and temporary. And the truth is *you are* all these wonderful things I've described, and more.

On offer here is everything you could possibly imagine and hope for. You have the opportunity of resting in the heart of all that is good. Simply by no longer buying into the illusion of what you're not, you can discover the pristine peace and unbounded beauty of *what you've been* the entire time.

Peace is your most natural way to be
It actually takes effort and causes the body stress to *not* be peaceful. The mind is the master and the body is the servant. The body follows the mind. Leading scientists have found stress to be one of the main

causes of physical conditions. The body heals more quickly and functions optimally when it is resting, or in other words, at peace.

You were <u>not</u> put on this planet to get sick.
You were born to live.

You were born to live a breathtakingly awe-inspiring life! You have the potential and opportunity to both feel fantastic and manifest a magnificent reality. Your most natural way of being is to experience perfect peace, limitless love, heaps of happiness and total completeness, without needing any specific reasons to do so. We are taught we need to *do* things to *be* all these great things. This simply is not true. The reality is quite the opposite. Simply resting back into what I refer to as your Real Self, you can get everything you could possibly want.

This isn't optimistic. It's not magic.
It is simply your birthright.

Isn't it a relief to recognise truth? Your heart knows this to be true. It responds to these words. Let that inner knowing be your guide. Trust your heart. Question your head. Because what you are going to discover is that peace is available to you now; by learning to think less, be present, and explore what exists beyond the confines of your mind.

The peace that's always present

Within your awareness, right now, is the on-going existence of a still silent space. A peace. However you can miss it because you've forgotten it's there.

Growing up you were encouraged to put 100% of your attention on the movement of your mind, your body and your life. You were rarely, if ever educated in the enlightening truth that absolutely everything happens within a constant context of pure and perfect, still silent awareness. In other words, how your mind, your body and your world all exist within an infinite and on-going presence of peace.

So you can end up missing the peace that is your birthright to enjoy. You feel what you focus on. So by putting your attention on things in your awareness that constantly move, are forever changing, and by their very nature, are in a constant state of flux, you end up feeling uneasy. Not only that, but because you end up missing a huge piece of yourself and reality, you can end up living with a sense that something is missing; that there must be more to life than what you are currently experiencing. Can you relate to this?

Closer than your next breath

The peace you seek is always present. It exists only now. However, because you've been taught to think about the past and future, you can end up in your mind, one step removed from the peace that's present. The good news is that the peace you seek is right under your nose. Closer than your next breath. It is you. It is here. And irrespective of how long you may have been distracted from it, it only takes an instant to return home.

My primary message to you within Part 3 is this:

Put your attention back on the still silent space that resides within your awareness right now and you will instantly reconnect with the pristine peace that is always present.

The path of peace is through a silent doorway of stillness. By bringing your attention back to the stillness that exists, always now, you immediately rest in the unbounded beauty and peaceful presence that is your Real Self.

Today you embark on a journey of freedom, which has been known for a very long time as the Path of the Sages, the Path of Return, the Path of the Hero and the Path of Joy. It is all these things and more. What you are going to learn is simple, but please don't underestimate its importance and magnitude. Knowing your Real Self is the purpose for which you were born.

CHAPTER EIGHT
Let go of what you think you know

Ever looked into the eyes of a baby? It's lovely, isn't it? One of the reasons why you enjoy it so much is that you recognise something. Something you've known but perhaps forgotten. What you see is undiluted consciousness aware of the present moment. The baby's mind is empty. It has no beliefs. It isn't judging. It isn't thinking to itself, 'Jeez, she needs to get her roots re-done!' or, 'wow, he's put on a few kilos'. Nope, nothing like that. It's not thinking. Instead, it is just innocently observing.

Innocent, with absolutely zero expectations, it is fully experiencing whatever it is aware of now. Fully connected to unbounded awareness it holds nothing and is completely open to whatever happens next. And because the baby hasn't yet learnt beliefs about how life *should* look, it is able to be open and fully experience the fullness of each moment.

Learning to be innocent again

For you to get what's on offer here, you need to see beyond your conditioned mind by being completely innocent with me now. Leave any opinions, ideas and past experiences at the door. There is no place for them in this entirely new moment.

Explore what it is like to bring nothing into this moment with you. Start to innocently observe what's happening now as if you don't know what's going to happen next. Because in reality you don't know what's going to happen. You just *think* you do. And thinking stops you from directly experiencing what is *actually* happening in reality. Thinking acts as a vial that stands between what you *think you are* and the true wonders of *what you really are*; and what life is.

There is a world of difference between knowing about peace and actually experiencing peace.

Play with having no pre-conceived ideas about how peace of mind is achieved. Knowledge knows *about* what you want, but where you're headed is the *direct experience* of what you want. Get the difference?

Would you prefer to know about your favourite food or do you want to taste it? Do you want to know about the present moment or do you want to *be* present? Do you want to know about peace or do you want to experience it?

You could have memorized an entire library of books about peace, but still not be *experiencing* peace. (Trust me, I tried!) Knowledge can only take you so far. There is always a point where you must be willing to let go of what you think you know to experience where the mind can only direct you to, but never experience.

Trust that nothing in the past is worth thinking about and nothing in the future could possibly be any better than what you are experiencing right now. Be with me now *as if* you don't know anything of value to help you experience this moment any better. Let go of expectations of how things should be. Let go of the notion you know *how life works*. Free yourself from future expectations. They only dull your experience of the magnificent moment you're in.

Innocence is fresh. It is utterly open, holds nothing, and is completely empty. If you are full of concepts and ideas about life then there is no space for you to experience truth. And the truth is that the Kingdom of Heaven is at hand. You arrived the day you were born. And you were born with peace, love and joy **built in**. But have been lead to believe you have to wait until things are different before you can experience what is your birthright to enjoy right now. Letting go of what you think you know helps you to step beyond the concepts of the mind to directly experience the truth (and peace) that is present.

Return to innocence

Remember the innocent baby whose mind is empty of judgments, beliefs and expectation? Over the next few days you are going to explore what it is like to play with being innocent again.

GAME #1
Fresh eyes

Explore what it is like to be completely fresh and innocent with the people in your life. See them with fresh eyes. Let go of any preconceived ideas you may have about your partner, parent(s), family member and friends, colleagues and even strangers. Just be with them fully, giving them your 100% attention. Like it's the first and last time you will get to be in their company. Don't try to manipulate any specific outcome from your interactions. Be open to whatever naturally wants to occur.

Pretend there is no past. You have no history with anyone. Pretend the people in your life are perfect exactly as they are. That they just want to be happy, experience peace and know they are loved. Your sole task this week is to interact with people with no judgments or expectations. Look with fresh eyes and note what you discover in your journal.

GAME #2
Making the mundane magical

Play with what it is like to be completely fresh and innocent with any mundane tasks you do this week; doing the dishes, the daily commute to work, having a shower, putting your make up on, tying your tie etc. Pretend it's the first time you have ever done these things and be fresh and innocent.

You are playing with forgetting something is boring, a person is difficult or anything should happen in any particular way. You are letting go of the notion you think you've figured out this thing called Life. Be innocent like a child, curious, and open to whatever happens. Note your observations in your journal.

CHAPTER NINE
Beyond conventional thinking

How many thoughts pass through your mind on a daily basis? Incredibly, it has been said the average person has around 100,000 thoughts every day – approximately one thought every second. That's a lot of thoughts! Perhaps more worryingly though, is the amount of these thoughts that are negative and, thus, are having a potentially harmful impact on your body, your emotions and your life.

Having observed the content of my own mind during countless hours of meditation and listened to literally hundreds of other people's minds when doing Mind Detox, I believe it would be very fair to suggest that at least half of the average person's thinking is negative. Does that percentage sound reasonable to you? It certainly did to me, at least until I realised 50% worked out at a massive 50,000 negative thoughts a day! Making any attempts to think *only* positive thoughts a monumental task.

The myth of positive thinking

Now I'm a believer in, and promoter of, the benefits of being positive. However, the sheer quantity of thoughts makes any attempts to *change your mind* so that you ONLY have 'positive thoughts' an almost impossible task. So be easy on yourself if you've done your best to think positive, but not mastered it. Such a quest is made even trickier by the fact that most of your thoughts pass through your mind without you having any control over them whatsoever. So is it a lost cause? No!

There is a solution that is very appealing indeed

Rather than attempt the impractical task of changing the thousands of negative thoughts that may pass through your mind on a daily basis, I recommend you do one thing: change your relationship *with* the thousands of thoughts. The goal: to experience peace irrespective of the kinds of thoughts that pass though your mind in any given moment.

Changing your relationship with your mind

Most people I meet spend their days jumping from thought to thought and experiencing a rollercoaster of emotions as a direct consequence. Much of their stress is the direct result of them being completely focused on the *content* of their mind rather than the *context* in which the movement of their mind happens. They are focused on their thoughts, rather than the vast silent stillness in which their thoughts take place.

Imagine you are outside on a clear sunny day, looking up at the sky. Then, out of the blue, a bird flies across your field of vision. Without realising you take your attention away from the vast sky and follow the flight of the bird. The same happens in your awareness every day. Thoughts are something you are aware of. Thoughts are movement in your awareness, yet, they all happen within the context of infinite still, silent, space. By learning to let your attention rest on the stillness, rather than on the constant movement, you can experience a peace far beyond what you ever thought possible.

Peace of mind with a million thoughts

Until you become the master of your mind, your mind is the master of you. You will find yourself feeling up and down like a yoyo depending on the quality of thoughts passing through your mind. If your mind produces happy thoughts you feel happy. If sad thoughts pass through you feel sad. If confident thoughts happen you stand tall, but if fearful thoughts flood in, you can want to run scared.

Thoughts happen, but if you are 100% engaged in the movement of your mind you will react like a puppet on strings. The good news is it doesn't have to be this way.

Your peace need not be dependent upon the quality of your thoughts.

Changing your relationship *with* your mind makes it possible for you to have negative thoughts without them affecting your peace in the slightest. Imagine that. You're mind doesn't need to affect your peace any longer.

Your mind can become like a radio on in the background, whereby you tune into the songs you enjoy (the thoughts that are useful to you), and tune out of the bad news (the downward spiralling thoughts that lead to stress, suffering and separation). You can go through your day resting in peace, free. Better news still, you already possess an important skill to be able to do what I'm suggesting.

Have you ever been out with a friend at a busy bar or restaurant where, despite the noise, you've been able to ignore the people talking right beside you by focusing your attention on the voice of your friend? (Or maybe the stranger beside you has had a more interesting conversation than your friend so you've ended up tuning out your friend to listen to the other person?!). In both of these scenarios you have directed your attention where you've wanted it. The same skill is required for enjoying peace with a mind full of thoughts.

Ultimately, when it comes to you enjoying inner peace, it's how you relate to your mind that matters. The moment you become aware of and place your attention upon what I will refer in this book as your *Real Self - the still conscious awareness that is silently aware of whatever is happening right now,* you will find that there is instantly more peace than a moment prior. What's more, you will then have the power to cultivate a life lived in a state of pristine peace, boundless bliss and constant contentment, amid a sea of what can be best described as pure, deep and limitless love.

Sound good? Let's get started in helping you to change your relationship with your mind.

You have thoughts, but *you* are not your thoughts
Peace of mind is possible whilst having thoughts because you are not your thoughts. Remember, thousands of thoughts pass through your awareness every day. They are constantly coming and going. It's what thoughts do. Thoughts appear for only a

moment, then disappear to be replaced with another thought, and then another one.

Yet, despite countless thoughts coming and going today, there has been an aspect to you that has been here the entire time. An aspect to *you* that is permanent. That's your Real Self. It is continually present, irrespective of the quality or quantity of thoughts that come and go. This undeniable fact means one very important truth: You *have* thoughts but *you* are not your thoughts.

LET'S PLAY A GAME
Counting thoughts

But don't take my word for it. Stop reading for a minute to close your eyes and watch your mind quietly observe the thoughts flowing through your mind. Then, whenever you become aware of a thought; which could be about this topic, something you need to do later, or whatever, simply give the thought a number: 1, 2, 3 and so on. Awareness of a sound occurring is a thought. Awareness of a physical sensation is a thought. Even the voice in your head saying you aren't having any thoughts is a thought! So make sure you count them all. See how many thoughts you can count over the next two minutes.

STOP READING AND DO IT NOW.

Having done that, how many thoughts did you count, 2, 22, 202?! It really doesn't matter how many. What matters is the fact you could even count one thought. Why? Because it means *you* cannot be your thoughts. Instead, *you* are that which is aware of your thoughts. There is a thought (an object) and *you* (the observer of the thought). One is constant, whereas the other is constantly changing. Thoughts come and go. But *you* don't.

You are that which is aware of your thoughts. You are not your thoughts! What a relief.

Incidentally, *you* are not your emotions either
Emotions come and go too, but your Real Self does not. The chances are you've had a range of emotions pass through your body during the past few hours. Similar to thoughts, emotions happen, but only for a while before they move on to be replaced by some other emotion. I appreciate that some emotions appear to be more comfortable than others. Yet, what's more important when it comes to you experiencing peace is the undeniable fact that emotions are temporary. And there is an aspect to you that is permanently in existence throughout your day. Yes, you have emotions, but *you* are not your emotions. Due to this, it is possible to change your relationship with your emotions to the extent that you can enjoy peace, irrespective of how you happen to be feeling. Again, imagine that!

How are you feeling?

Now, for you to be able to answer this simple question, you need to observe whatever emotion is currently occurring within your body. The emotion becomes the object, and *you* the observer of the emotion. Not only that, but also by observing the emotion you naturally create some space between *you* and the emotion. From this perspective, you can start to recognize, from your first hand experience, that *you* are not your emotions. Yes, you *have* emotions, but the permanent *you* is not emotional.

Emotional liberation

Emotions only become problematic if you *become* your emotions. Thinking *you* are your emotions, you then engage in mental analysis trying to figure-out why they are happening and what you can do to fix them. But the truth is your emotions don't need to be fixed. It's only your relationship with them that does.

Freedom from emotional turmoil can be very close if you begin to explore your relationship with your emotions. Irrespective of what emotions occur, you can let them come and go and experience very little stress or discomfort as they pass through - *if you remember to observe them instead of being them*. The reality is your Real Self is untouched by any temporary emotion. It has never been happy or sad, scared or guilty. Conscious awareness is permanently peaceful and beyond the emotional realm. Let's explore this with a game…

Watching Emotions

While we are on the topic of emotions, let play another game. You can do this game any time you are experiencing an emotion that you would rather not. It is amazingly effective at helping emotions dissolve - quickly - so you can more easily cultivate your relationship with peace.

You can also play with this game if you are feeling positive too, because it can help you to discover your Real Self – the aspect to *you* that is beyond the emotional realm. Here are the instructions:

STEP #1: **NAME IT**

Notice what you are feeling right now. Are you feeling happy, sad, angry or anxious or something else? Simply tune in and notice what emotion you are currently feeling.

STEP #2: **LOCATE IT**

Locate it in your body. What area of your body is it mainly located? Is it in your stomach, solar plexus, heart or chest or some other place in your body? Locate it now.

STEP #3: **COLOUR IT**

Once you have located the emotion, give it a colour. Any colour will do. Red, green, violet, black, blue – it really does not matter. Just go with your first answer. Colour the emotion now.

STEP #4: **WATCH IT**

Now you've named it, located it and given the emotion a colour, simply watch it being there. As if you have double-sided eyes: look backward, downward and within to watch the coloured emotion at that location in your body. Just watch it. Remember to keep breathing deeply and in a balanced way as you do this. Continue watching and notice what happens to the emotion. For me, whenever I do this, after a few seconds of watching, the emotion always disperses. Like water on a hot plate, or the sun parting clouds, the emotion evaporates. That's right, it simply disappears!

Why this game works

As you grew up you were taught what emotions were 'good' and which were 'bad'. This has conditioned you to resist 'bad' emotions whenever you notice them occurring. But as the well-known phrase goes – *'what you resist persists'*. Alternatively, by turning your attention towards your emotions, through the simple act of watching, you can cause them to disappear. Why? Because when you watch the emotion you stop *being* the emotion.

Start observing your emotions, you immediately create space (between *you* and the emotions) that gives them a chance to flow and go – as they naturally want to do. Further more, when you watch your emotions you become aware. When you become aware, you start to experience what your *own awareness* is like. Beyond the emotional realm, you discover your conscious awareness is always pristinely peaceful - irrespective of what temporary emotions happen to be occurring within your body.

More aware of your Real Self, than your temporary emotional self, you immediately begin to experience the peace that is always present. Amazing isn't it! Doing this simple exercise can help you to be less fearful of your feelings, stop being governed by your emotions and enjoy emotional freedom. **Use it!**

Let's make sure we are on the same page

There is an aspect to *you* that is permanent. You also have thoughts and emotions that are only temporary. The purpose of this chapter is to introduce you to the possibility that you can change your relationship with your mind so that your thoughts and emotions can exist without them impacting upon your peace.

This is possible because *you* are not your thoughts and emotions. Instead, *you* are that which is aware of your thoughts and emotions occurring - and that awareness is still and silent and beyond the mind. By becoming aware, you start to experience what your *own awareness* is like. Which is, yes you guessed it, peaceful. Freedom comes from you learning how to put most of your attention on your own peaceful awareness, rather than being solely focused on what you are aware of.

By making this shift in where you put your attention, you reconnect with the aspect of your Real Self that is permanently peaceful.

TOP TIP
Thinking about *versus* directly experiencing

There is a huge difference between *thinking about* this game and actually doing it now. If you do it, immediately, then it will work for you – it has for 100% of the people I've used it with! However, if you *think about* doing it, then you are going to end up in your head, one step removed from the direct experience of what it is I'm showing you.

The same goes for everything else I talk about in this book. It is very easy to unwittingly slip into your mind to start evaluating and judging what's being said, rather than going beyond the confines of your mind to directly experience what I'm saying. So if any of the games don't work for you, check in to see if - in that moment - you are actually doing them, or just thinking about doing them.

There's a massive difference between *thinking* and *experiencing* and your peace is dependent upon you knowing the difference.

For the next week at least, play with these games:

GAME #1
Counting Thoughts

Three times each day, (before breakfast, before your evening dinner, and before bed), I want you to stop for two minutes, close your eyes and count your thoughts. Notice what happens when you count your thoughts. Note your observations.

GAME #2
Watching Emotions

Whenever you notice yourself feeling positive or negative emotions, stop for a few moments to do the Watching Emotions game. Name it, locate it, colour it and watch it. Notice what happens. Remember, there's a big difference between thinking about watching and actually watching. If the emotions are ever intense, the chances are you've identified with the emotions instead of watching them.

By doing these exercises whenever you remember, you have the chance of discovering that *you* are not your thoughts and emotions. This is a massive step in improving your relationship with your mind. Remember, this entire book is about helping you to *experience* peace. So the more you practice with the games, the more you will ultimately benefit. *Jump in!*

CHAPTER TEN
Peace is only experienced now

Life is happening right now. Now is all there is. It is forever new and fresh and full and vibrant. Everything that exists within reality exists only now. Now is the only moment that exists. The only moment *you* exist. And the only moment you can *ever* experience inner peace.

This chapter is about letting go of the notion that anything needs to change, be fixed or improved **before** you can enjoy peace. It's about no longer letting your peace be dependent on your past or future by learning to let *this* moment be enough.

The hidden barrier to your peace

Peace is always present. It truly is. However, you can end up missing it if you are in your head thinking. This is because although peace exists now, your mind only exists by thinking about the past and future. Thinking acts as an invisible barrier that stands between you and the present moment, between you and the experience of peace. I say *invisible* because most people aren't aware of the impact thinking has on their peace.

Thinking makes you numb to true peace because your mind is always one step removed from any given experience. The mind cannot experience the present moment, it can only think *about* the present moment. Similarly, the mind cannot experience peace, it can only think *about* peace. So as long as you continue to be *in your mind* thinking, your peace will remain out of reach.

Are you unnecessarily postponing your peace?

Due to the mind's inability to experience peace, it has no alternative but to postpone it. It assumes something must be wrong with life now and works tirelessly to find all the things that need to be fixed, changed or improved. It tells you that you must *do* x y or z in order to *be* peaceful and that you need to change your body, your finances, your relationships, your career, your environment... pretty much everything! All before you can enjoy some peace.

Not being aware of this tendency of the mind can cause you to end up victim to its never-ending postponement of your peace. The future never comes. So you can end up waiting for peace your entire life due to your mind's ability to endlessly think up new items to add to your things-I-need-to-do-so-I-can-eventually-enjoy-some-peace list!

Don't get me wrong; I'm not suggesting your mind is against you. Quite the opposite! It believes by helping you to change your body and your life that *one day* you will be able to enjoy peace. But here lies the problem.

Your mind will always put your peace in the future because it cannot experience it now.

There are no present moment thoughts

Before I learnt there was an alternative way of being, I spent most of my days lost in my mind thinking about the past and future. I would think about what *had happened* hours, days, weeks and even years ago, or mentally rehearse all the things that were *going to* *happen* hours, days, weeks or years in the future. Sound familiar?

One of the biggest insights I've discovered during countless hours of meditation and guidance from enlightened teachers is this: *There are no present moment thoughts.* Let me explain what I mean. For the mind to talk about something it needs to have happened. Even if that something appears to be happening now, it has to have *happened* for the mind to be able to talk (think) about it. So if you are thinking about the past and future, then you are missing the present moment.

Being present and being peaceful are one and the same. You cannot experience one without the other. Knowing this makes experiencing peace supremely simple and brilliantly clear-cut:

You are either in the moment experiencing peace or you're in your head thinking about peace.

Peace is not present in the past or future

Despite your peace only ever existing now, the potential exists for your attention to slip into the past and future via your mind. Going into the past is only possible by going into your imagination. The past is nothing more than a collection of old thoughts. Reality, on the other hand, is what's real, right now (I think this is why it's called **real**ity!)

So if you want to experience real peace, I recommend you don't waste a second intentionally thinking about past moments. You will not find peace there. Only here. Nor will you find peace in the future. The future might offer hope, but this moment delivers you home to the peace, love and joy that is your birthright to experience, explore and enjoy. Remember, even if you are successful in your quest to make your past and future perfect, you can still only ever *experience peace now*. So again, why waste your time deliberately thinking about the past or future if *experiencing peace now* is what you ultimately want?

This book is all about you *experiencing* peace and it is impossible for you to directly experience anything truly fulfilling in any time other than now. But don't take my word for it. Take time to consider your top three best moment of your entire life so far.

They will most probably have one thing in common – you were present. Time had ceased to exist. You were not thinking about the past or future. You were 100% present, giving your full attention to whatever was happening.

The great news is that by learning to be present, much of your life can be as fulfilling as your best moments.

The glorious gifts from being present

Believe it or not, what's happened in your past or what might happen in your future does not have to impact upon your current levels of peace. When you are fully present, then there is no time to dwell on the past, complain about the present, or wish for more in the future. You discover it is much more appealing to be here, in *this* moment, than think about the past or future. You notice that thinking about the past and future feels dead compared to the vibrancy of now.

You notice that once something has happened, it is immediately in the past. Gone. Forever, even if it happened only a moment ago. You stop holding on to the past or fighting what might happen in the future. You know that nothing in the past is worth thinking about and nothing in the future could possibly bring you more peace than being present.

It becomes the natural choice to make the most of this moment.

No longer relying on your future to give you anything, you let this moment be enough and experience perfect peace, limitless love, and heaps of happiness as a direct consequence. Fully present, you are not judging this moment or comparing it to a past or future moment. You experience life as being perfect, whole and complete. You rest fully in the peace that's always present.

TOP TIP
Being present practicalities

One of the most common confusions about being present is that you can no longer talk about the past and future. However, the good news is that you can talk about whatever you want.

From an ongoing awareness of the present moment, you are able to talk about what's happened in the past or plan for the future. (I do it all the time within the context of my work when sharing stories about the past and planning my courses and retreats.) However, the main difference is that you remain fully aware of the present moment, and from here, talk about whatever you want. The difference is that you don't leave the present moment to re-experience the past as you talk about it. Get the difference? The same goes for future plans too. You can be right here, right now, yet still plan for future events.

Play with it! You will find there's a huge difference when it comes to the levels of peace you enjoy. You will be able to talk about past events (even traumatic ones) without any emotional turmoil whatsoever because most of your attention is here, not there. You may also find that worrying about the future also falls away as you no longer need it to fulfil you. It is a very freeing way to be.

Whilst staying present, let's review the past chapter!
If you aren't enjoying as much peace, love, beauty, mystery, fun or happiness as you would like, then it doesn't mean these things aren't already present in your life. It just means you aren't present enough to experience them. By getting out of your thoughts and getting into the present moment, you can experience life as a wonderful gift.

Being present and being peaceful are intrinsicall linked. You cannot experience one without the othe Enjoying peace by living in the present moment i supremely simple and clear-cut: You are either in th moment *experiencing peace* or you are in your hea *thinking about* peace. The choice can be yours.

ACTIVITY
Peace Postponers

Explore what you believe needs to happen so you ca experience peace of mind. Be honest with yoursel when answering the following questions. Avoi editing your thoughts between your head and you hand. It is important that you see your unedite thoughts so you can challenge the ones that might b postponing your peace.

1. *What do I think needs to change about myself so I ca experience peace?* (Things to consider include th shape, weight and health of your body, your intellec your skills, your achievements, your failures, you past, your future etc.)

2. *What do I think needs to change about my life so I ca experience peace?* (Things to consider include you health, your relationships, your finances, you security, your responsibilities, your time pressure your career, and your living environment etc.)

3. *What do I think needs to change about myself in order for me to be 100% loveable?* (Things to consider include the shape, weight and health of your body, your intellect, your skills, your achievements, your failures, your past, your potential etc).

4. *What do I think needs to change about my life in order for me to love it completely?*

5. *What do I think needs to change in order for me to be completely content?*

BONUS QUESTION

What ideas do I have about enlightenment? (Things to consider include: What is an enlightened person like? How do they behave? What happens in their mind? Do they have thoughts? Do they have emotions? Is enlightenment possible in this lifetime for me?)

Having answered the above questions, now consider: *Are any of your answers conditions that are postponing your peace?*

By this I mean: are you waiting for things to be different, fixed or improved *before* you can enjoy peace, love and contentment? If you have found conditions, then great! It is important that you become aware of the things you *believe* must happen because these are the very thoughts you need to be willing to let go of in order to enjoy more peace now.

(You might want to use my 5-Step method to discover when you created these peace-postponing beliefs and let go of them, for good. Or you may also want to play with the Decision Destroyer technique in Appendix 3.)

The truth is that nothing needs to change about you or your life for you to experience peace. It is just a conditioned belief that tells you otherwise. Your mind will always put your peace in the future because it cannot experience it now. Yes, it can think about peace, but because it cannot experience it, it will constantly tell you things need to be different for you to experience peace.

You can end up missing peace your entire life if you believe your misinformed mind.

Freedom from problems and peace for life requires you to be OK irrespective of what's happening in your body, your mind and your life. In the next chapter I will share the missing piece of the peace of mind puzzle. You will learn one of my favourite ways to play with being present. In doing so, you can reconnect with the peace that's always present.

CHAPTER ELEVEN
The missing peace of the puzzle

Peace for life becomes possible if you understand and apply what I'm going to share now. For me, it was the missing piece of my peace of mind puzzle. So much so that after I properly *got* what you are about to *get* now, enjoying real peace in the real world became a living reality for me. There's no reason why the same cannot be the case for you too.

Being present is more than just noticing what you can see, hear, feel, smell and taste now. What you put your attention on matters hugely and is often overlooked. Peace can continue to elude you if your attention continues to be scattered. As people learn to be present in their daily lives it is common for their attention to jump from one thing to the next as they attempt to be aware of whatever is currently happening. However this is a very common reason why people miss the peace that's always present. To avoid this, you can learn how to be attentive to the underlying subjective reality of the present moment.

Bobbing around on the surface of a chaotic ocean

Like the surface of the ocean, your thoughts emotions, body, career, relationships, money and all other aspects of your external world are constantly changing. That's what they do.

Thoughts happen, emotions flow, the body does its thing. New people enter your life as others leave. Careers change, political parties rise and fall, and economic climates can change as quickly as the weather. Due to all these aspects of your body, your mind and your life being in a constant state of flux and to a large extent, out of your direct control, it is no wonder you don't find much peace there.

The power of where you put your attention

The good news is there is one thing in life that you have a high degree of control over, namely: where you put your attention. It is something nobody else can 100% control. It is something your external life circumstances need not dictate. Irrespective of what's happening to your body or in your life, you have the power to choose what you put you attention on in any given moment. This being the case, the next obvious question to ask is: *Where can you put your attention so you experience the most peace now?* The answer to this question is nothing less than enlightening!

Ultimately, there are only two things you can focus your attention on, namely: the outward content or the inward context of your life.

Let's assume for a moment that the entire universe exists within the room you are currently located. In that room there might be furniture, flowers, light fittings, your telephone, other belongings etc. The term I use to refer to all these things is STUFF. Now, for all the stuff to exist, there has to be the context of SPACE. In fact, there has to be more space than stuff, otherwise the stuff wouldn't fit in the space. And although the stuff can come and go, the space in which it inhabits is completely constant and unchanging.

CONTENT
Stuff

CONTEXT
Space

As you read these words you may become aware of SOUNDS around you. There might be the sounds of a clock ticking, birds singing, the hum of traffic in the distance, the shimmering of leaves outside your window, music playing, or people talking nearby. For these sounds to exist, they happen within a context of SILENCE. For you to hear anything there has to be the constant context of silence. Sound needs silence. Even if you are surrounded by noise, there is silence so you can hear the noise, and that silence resides within your awareness – now and always.

CONTENT	CONTEXT
Stuff	Space
Sounds	Silence

Furthermore, the content of your current experience also includes MOVEMENT. The movement of your chest as you breathe, the movement of your fingers as you progress through this book, the movement of the trees outside your window as the breeze continues to blow. Yet, again, the content of that movement happens within a context of absolute STILLNESS, a stillness that is untouched by any movement, ever.

CONTENT	CONTEXT
Stuff	Space
Sounds	Silence
Movement	Stillness

So we've discovered that the content of your life including all of the stuff, sounds and movement, all happen within a context of still silent space. Not only that, but the content comes and goes and is changing whereas the context is constantly present and unchanging. Incidentally, the same occurs within your mind too. The movement of your thoughts and emotions all occur within a constant context of still silent space.

Now the million-dollar question:

Where do you tend to focus most of your attention throughout your day - on the content or the context of your life?

Almost everyone I ask this question to sees clearly that they put most of their attention, most of the time, on the content of their mind and lives.

Naturally you feel what you focus on
So if you put all your attention on that which is moving and changing you will most likely experience a sense of instability and unease. However, reconnecting with the peace that's always present requires you to learn to put your attention on that which never moves or changes and is permanently still and silent.

Making this shift in where you put your attention immediately reconnects you with your birthright. Peace, contentment, love, happiness and so much more. It's waiting patiently for you. Waiting for you to become aware of its already present existence.

Your Real Self is the still silent conscious awareness that is aware of this moment happening. And that awareness is already at peace, perfectly contented and full of love. You are not separate from that, but you can take your attention away from it, by thinking about the past and future.

Remember this from now on

Looking for peace in your mind (by having no thoughts), in your emotions (by only feeling positive), in your physical body (by it being healthy and looking how you think it should), or in your career, money, relationships and any other aspects of your external life circumstances DOES NOT WORK *(You don't need to take my word for it; your own life experiences can be evidence enough!)* So if you have not found peace by looking to change, improve and perfect your body, your mind or your life, then it's probably time for a new strategy.

You feel what you focus on. By focusing on things that constantly change and are out of your control, is not surprising you haven't been feeling peaceful. However, by putting your attention on stillness, on space and on silence (whatever works best for you) you naturally experience peace.

It really can be as simple as that.

LET'S PLAY A GAME
Noticing the moment

Let's play a game to help you experience what I've been talking about. There are three golden rules for this game that you must adhere to if you want to reap the immediate benefits:

RULE #1: **You can't do this game wrong**.
So just play like a child. I remember as a kid I used to play for hours with a cardboard box and a couple spoons imagining I was in a boat. Now, I couldn't do it wrong because I was just playing. So don't try to get this right, just play and explore (innocently) and see what happens.

RULE #2: **You can't do it later.**
By this, I mean you can only do it now. So don't try to analyse what I'm asking you to do or plan to do it later. Instead, just do it, immediately.

RULE #3: **You can't think about doing it.**
You can only do it. If it isn't working for you, then you are in your mind thinking about it, instead of being in the moment experiencing what I'm inviting you to notice.

Happy with the rules? Great, let's get started!

As you are reading this I am going to assume you have a page in front of you, either printed or on a computer screen. I want you to keep looking at the page as you notice your left shoulder. To notice it you don't need to look at it or move it, just tune in and notice your left shoulder.

OK? Easy? Perfect. Let's continue.

Now notice your right foot. Again, you can keep looking ahead at the page as you notice your right foot. You can keep reading. You don't need to wiggle your toes or anything like that. You can simply take your attention to your right foot and notice it now.

OK? Still easy? Great. Let's continue.

Now, without trying to figure out what I'm asking you to do, I want you to notice the space between you and this page. Just do that now. You don't have to look around between you and the page, just keep looking ahead and simply notice that the space exists between you and the page. It's been there the entire time; all you are doing now is noticing it is there as you continue to keep your gaze forward at the page.

Still easy? OK, let's continue playing.

Now I want you to notice the space around the page. Don't look directly around the page; keep looking directly ahead as you notice the space around it

Notice the space around the page for a few moments before continuing.

You are doing great.

Now I want you to notice the space in the entire room. Like a switch in your awareness, let your attention notice the space in the entire room. As you do that, I want you to notice what it's like to do this.

What's your inner experience like as you notice the space in the entire room? Remember, keep your gaze forward and don't look around the room trying to find or see the space. Trust me, its there. All I want you to do is notice the space in the entire room. As you continue to do this, what word or words could you use to describe what your experience is like as you notice the space now?

I've asked literally hundreds of people to do this. Common answers include: calm, peaceful, still, open, expansive, light, comforting, home, freeing and so on. As you notice the space in the entire room, what word(s) could *you* use to describe what it's like to notice the space?

QUICK TIP
Don't stop noticing the space to try to describe it because that will start you thinking and stop you experiencing. Just notice and trust your first words.

Let's continue.

Now I want you to notice that *this moment is happening*. That you are sitting where you are, reading *this* word. Observing *this word* being read. And now *this word*. Simply notice this moment is happening. What's it like to quietly notice? To do nothing other than gently watch this moment occurring. What words could you use to describe what your experience is like as you do this? Again, common words are calm, peaceful, quiet, still, spacious, open, free and so on.

Experiencing what it's like to be aware
Well done. This exercise helps you to become aware by noticing. When you become aware you become present because your awareness that is noticing is always present. Your awareness is always present. It can only ever be aware of *this* moment. Even if you are not aware of your awareness, (due to getting distracted by thought and emotions about the past and future) your awareness remains permanently aware of this moment – only and always – a silent watcher watching from behind your eyes. Furthermore, when you become present, you immediately start to directly experience what *your awareness* is like. Because awareness is by its very nature – still and silent and spacious – you start to experience exactly that. Or in other words, you start to experience more calmness, peace, quietness, expansiveness and more.

For the benefit of any doubt
The mind is movement. It consists of thoughts about the past and future that come and go. Your mind cannot mimic the experience of still silent space. This means you are genuinely beyond your mind, in the present moment, when you are placing most of your attention on the presence of still silent space now.

Knowing this helps to avoid confusion as to when you are present or not. Allowing you to be confident that if you are ever thinking about whether you are present, then in that moment, you can be sure that you're not!

ACTIVITY
Practice makes permanent

Play with this *noticing the moment* exercise as much as possible. Notice the space between you and other people when you are talking to them, or the space between you and your computer etc. Notice the space around objects, whether that's people, your cup of tea or your TV. Notice the space in the entire rooms you are in, whether that be the office, the supermarket or your kitchen. Notice, notice notice! Remember the three golden rules and pretend it is your first time each time you do it.

You may notice that *every time* you do it there's more peace than a moment before (when you weren't aware). Perhaps more importantly, you will notice it works every time. Why is this so important? Because you have the opportunity of discovering that when you become aware, you become present, and when you are present, you experience peace. How amazing is that?

Peace never left you; you left peace!

By playing with this game consistently you can notice that you experience a presence of peace every time you become aware of the underlying reality of the present moment. That your awareness is the permanent aspect to you and your awareness is still, silent and peaceful. Beautifully, you can discover peace never left you. Rather, you left peace simply by taking your attention away from this moment.

TOP TIP
Permanent peace starts now

Desiring permanent peace is natural and wonderful. The remarkable news is that permanent peace is possible. Yet, despite this exciting possibility, always remember…

Life is only ever happening now so peace for life is 100% about being peaceful now.

If you want your experience of peace to be permanent then simply make it your number one priority to be inwardly attentive to still silent space now.

Let the future take care of itself. The only thing that matters is where your attention is right now. *Are you putting most of your attention on movement or stillness, sound or silence, stuff or space?* If you find yourself caring whether your peace is permanent or not it means your attention has slipped away from the presence of peace now and gone into the future via your mind. Be here now. Be still now. And you will find your peace is permanent – it always has been!

PEACE FOR LIFE

CHAPTER TWELVE
10 myths about meditation

Meditation serves many purposes, from simple stress relief to full enlightenment. Personally, I started meditating because I was fed up with my mind working overtime. I wanted peace and through meditating regularly I have become less focused on the movement of my mind and much more aware of the pristine peace that is always present.

Reconnect with your Real Self

Meditation helps you to become aware of the essence of *what* you are. It works by helping you to change your relationship with your mind. You stop *being* your mind (fully engaged in thoughts and emotions), by learning to watch without engagement. Through

the practice of watching, you start to become awar
of the awareness that is watching. You notice you
awareness is still, silent and untouched by an
temporary movement of the mind – completely out o
harms way from any external threat. With regula
practice and guidance, you can live free from fea
fully aware you are one with the Source of Love.

10 myths about meditation

Despite meditation being so simple, and having suc
big rewards, there are some myths about meditatio
that can stop people getting started or make then
quit before they get to reap the benefits possible from
meditating regularly. In this chapter I want to shar
what these myths are and teach you a simple way o
meditating to help you get started.

MYTH #1
Meditation is difficult

Practiced correctly, meditation can be the easiest and
most enjoyable thing you ever do. For something to
be difficult, it requires effort, struggle, stress and
stamina. However, the truth is meditation require
the exact opposite. There is no effort because you are
learning how to do nothing. There is no struggle
because you are not forcing anything. There is no
stress because you are not resisting anything and

there is no need for stamina because the main purpose of meditation is to relax!

MYTH #2
I must still my mind

'I can't meditate because I can't stop my thoughts' is one of the most common reasons I hear from people who've tried meditation but quit. However, what's important to understand is that thoughts are a natural (and necessary) part of meditation.

When you meditate your body gets rest. When the body rests it heals. Healing is an active process – stress is released and healing is being undertaken. Due to the mind-body connection, activity in your body is reflected by activity in your mind – in the form of thoughts. Thoughts are therefore a sign that healing is taking place in your body.

Healing your nervous system is a fantastic by-product of meditation. It is not useful to resist having thoughts when meditating. To resist thoughts is to resist healing! Instead, let the healing process happen, as it naturally wants to, by not resisting the existence of thoughts.

Thoughts are a necessary part of meditation.
Thoughts are natural. Thoughts are OK!

MYTH #3
If thoughts are OK, then it's OK to think

Although having thoughts is OK, I am <u>NOT</u> recommending you *intentionally* think your way through every meditation. There is a big difference between having thoughts and thinking. When you are meditating you want to let thoughts flow through your awareness without engaging in them through the act of thinking.

Thinking occurs when you stop *observing* your thoughts and you start *being* your thoughts. When you are thinking you are in the thought stream. You are in the dream. Engaged in the story of your mind, you are having an imaginary conversation with your friend, planning what you're going to have for dinner, or whatever.

Thinking is very similar to falling asleep.

When you are thinking, you are essentially lost in your mind. You are no longer present, nor consciously aware of your Real Self. Thinking is a habit you learn to do less of through the regular practice of meditation. Be gentle on yourself if you find yourself thinking when meditating. It's just a habit! When you become aware that you've been thinking, simply come back to being alert, present and watching.

MYTH #4
I have to *feel* peaceful

Be careful not to fall into the common trap of thinking a peaceful meditation is better than an emotional one. Similar to thoughts (in Myth #2), having emotions when meditating is a sign of stress releasing from your body and healing taking place. Also, remember that emotions are only ever temporary, but the presence of peace is permanent. Emotions exist within the *content* of your mind, but your peace is the *context* of your mind. It is a fascinating experience when you begin to notice you can simultaneously have a negative emotion whilst being perfectly at peace. Meditation reveals this freeing experience through regular practice.

MYTH #5
Meditation stops when I open my eyes

Most of your day will be spent with your eyes open so thankfully the little flaps of skin you call your eye lids do not need to impact upon your peace. Peace is experienced when you put your attention on the still silent space within your awareness. You can direct your attention with your eyes open and closed. One goal of meditation is to develop the habit of effortlessly having some of your awareness looking inwards on still silent space at all times. Eyes open or closed – it need not matter.

MYTH #6
It's pointless trying because I fall asleep

Your body will do what it needs to do when you meditate – if it needs sleep then you will sleep. That is perfectly fine and if you continue to meditate regularly you will find that the need for sleep may reduce as you learn to be less stressed during daily life. If you find yourself falling asleep *every time*, then you might want to experiment with the following ways of staying more alert during meditation:

- ✓ Meditate at times of the day when you know you are more likely to be awake
- ✓ Sit more upright (you can still be comfortable with the right support)
- ✓ Do some exercise before meditating so that you are physiologically more alert.

MYTH #7
I have to breathe a certain way to meditate

Many forms of meditation encourage participants to focus on their breath. There are also many that don't. Focusing on the breath can help you be less focused on the mind, but it is certainly not an absolute necessity when meditating. (Personally, the form of meditation I use does not rely on the breath, but I do find breathing to be very useful indeed!)

MYTH #8
I have to concentrate hard

Peace, joy, love, contentment and freedom are all the natural by-products of being consciously aware rather than being unaware, lost in your mind (thinking). The good news is meditation takes very little effort because it takes zero effort to be aware. You are *already* aware. It is *what* you are. Whether you are aware of it yet, or not!

MYTH #9
Visualization is the same as meditation

Meditation helps you to experience more peace by moving your attention away from the movement of your mind to the still silent space within your awareness. Guided visualizations, on the other hand, require you to focus your attention on the mind. So although guided visualizations may by fun, they do not lead to permanent peace.

Remember, the mind is movement so it cannot mimic stillness or silence. So when your attention is on still silence you are resting beyond the mind. Being beyond the mind means you are beyond limitation, beyond judgments and beyond problems. Being beyond your mind means you are resting in the heart of all that is good.

MYTH #10
It takes a long time to enjoy any benefits

You start benefiting from meditation from th
moment you begin. You might not experienc
immediate peace or joy, but your body will get
chance to rest, release stored stress and heal. Thi
myth reminds me of a story. A 70-year-old ma
wanted to learn to play piano. His son questione
what the point was because it takes so long to learr
However the piano-playing pensioner wasn
persuaded to quit. Instead he simply told his so
that if he started now he'd be a much better pian
player by age 75 than if he didn't start at all!

I love this story because it is very much the same fc
meditation. It may take a little time to experienc
highly noticeable changes. But if you start, and kee
doing it regularly, you can be sure you will b
experiencing much more peace, love and happines
over the coming months and years, compared to
you never start at all.

BONUS MYTH
Meditation is boring

Whether something is boring, or not, is a matter c
opinion and your opinions exist in your mind. B
ignoring thoughts and emotions associated wit
boredom you can more quickly enjoy mind mastery.

ACTIVITY
Mind Mastery Meditation

Three simple steps to get started meditating:

STEP #1
Relax

Thankfully you don't have to sit like a pretzel cross-legged on the cold floor of a cave somewhere in the Himalayas to successfully meditate! You can do it very well in the comfort of your own home on a seat, sofa or even lying on your bed. Wear loose clothes, support yourself with comfy cushions and wrap yourself in a blanket if there's a chance you could get chilly. Actually, do whatever it takes to be comfortable (but not so comfortable you are inevitably going to go to sleep!).

STEP #2
Watch

Once you are perfectly comfortable, gently close your eyes whilst remaining alert. From the here and now, let your attention rest wide as you watch whatever is happening within your awareness, right now. This takes no effort, no straining or trying.

Continue by very easily, comfortably and gently observing your thoughts as they flow through your

mind – as if they are passing clouds in the vast sky
By watching your mind, instead of *being* your mind
you are changing your relationship with your mind.

STEP #3
Allow

Pretend you are having a holiday from your head
You have nothing to do except sit back and relax
Never resist thoughts; they are a natural-by-produc
of stress releasing from your body. Irrespective o
what the thoughts are, let them come and go. Yo
are officially off duty so they are not your problem
The quantity of thoughts doesn't matter. The conten
of the thoughts doesn't matter. They might be pretty
thoughts. They might be negative thoughts. Jus
allow your mind to do whatever it wants. Simpl
watch and allow. Out of habit you might star
thinking. When you become aware that you ar
thinking, gently come back to watching and allowing

Noticing still silent space
As you meditate, you may become aware of
quietness or stillness or openness. This is you
conscious awareness, your Real Self. It is good to le
your attention move to the stillest quietest part o
your experience so you can cultivate a more intimat
relationship with your Real Self.

Ideally, I recommend 10-20 minutes of meditation 2 or 3 times every day; before breakfast in the morning, before your evening meal, and before bed. Through short and regular stints of meditation throughout your day you can learn to be more present, release stored stress and become increasingly aware of a constant context of still silent peace. It's worth it!

BONUS TIP
Meditation works!

That's why it's been around for thousands of years. And it will work for you if you keep doing it. The only reason you will stop meditating (and miss out on all the benefits) is if you believe your mind when it says one of the following thoughts:

I don't have enough time today
I can't meditate
I'm having too many thoughts
I'm not feeling peaceful
This isn't working
I think I will stop and try again later

Don't be fooled
If you ever have any thoughts like the ones above that could talk you out of meditating then I recommend you laugh at them and continue meditating. Freedom comes from not being ruled by your conditioned mind. Happy meditating!

CHAPTER THIRTEEN
Make peace your priority

During the past chapters you have discovered:

✓ Innocence sits at the heart of enjoying peace for life. To be innocent is to let go of what you think you know, especially when it comes to what you think has to be changed, fixed or improved *before* you can enjoy peace.

✓ You do not need to postpone your peace until a future moment in time when things are how you think they *should* be.

✓ Instead of spending years trying to change your mind so that you only have positive thoughts and emotions, by moving beyond conventional thinking by changing your relationship *with* your mind, you can experience peace immediately.

- ✓ The quality or quantity of the thoughts and emotions passing through your mind need not impact your peace in any way whatsoever.
- ✓ Your Real Self is the *permanent* still silent awareness that is aware of your *temporary* thoughts and emotions, physical body and external life circumstances.
- ✓ Your conscious awareness is beyond the physical, mental and emotional realms, void of problems and permanently peaceful.
- ✓ Although peace can only be experienced now, your mind always postpones peace because your mind is one step removed from the peace that's always present.
- ✓ Experiencing peace requires you to be beyond the mind by being fully present.
- ✓ By placing your attention on the still silent space within your awareness you move your attention away from the constant chatter of your mind, and instead, become present and experience peace.
- ✓ Contentment is the direct result of letting this moment be enough, exactly as it is.
- ✓ Being peaceful does not mean you become passive. By letting your attention rest inward on still silence, it is still possible to proactively make positive changes to your life.
- ✓ By meditating regularly, ideally three times every day, you can change the habit of thinking to a new habit of being aware of the still silent context of your body, your mind and your life. In doing so, you can experience ever-increasing levels of peace in your life.

An enlightening few pages I hope you agree!

Yet despite knowing these powerful insights and having started to experience some peace using the games shared, this final chapter is by far the most important of all.

Applying what you are about to learn helps you to *enjoy long-lasting and ever-increasing peace.* This is because, although we are coming to the end of this book, your life continues. Unexpected physical conditions may arise, misunderstandings may occur, deadlines may be tight and other problems might happen. However, irrespective of what life brings, you need to be willing to take your attention away from the content of your stressed mind and instead, place it on the still silent peace always residing within your awareness. A choice that only becomes possible if you...

Make peace your priority

I appreciate it might sound rather simplistic, but when you know *how* to experience peace, the main thing that stands between you and your peace is your priorities. Take a moment to consider:

How important is my peace?

What things are more important than being peaceful? Is experiencing peace today more important than having a different past or a better future? Is peace more important

than having better health? Is money and possessions mor
important than peace?

Put a price on your peace

Although this suggestion may sound rathe
unspiritual at first glance, I'm serious when it come
to putting a monetary value on your peace. I used t
get upset over a £30 parking ticket. When I did, I wa
unwittingly valuing my peace of mind at a mer
£29.99 (or less!). I was willing to exchange m
precious peace for the price of a parking ticket. Ho
silly! To help you avoid making similar mistakes, I'r
going to share some of the most common thing
people (unintentionally) make more important tha
their peace of mind:

REASON #1
Being right

Stop trying to be right – it's not only stressful, but it'
more often than not, pointless. The more you becom
consciously aware of the present moment and re
discover your Real Self, the more it becomes clea
that there is a big difference between relative an
absolute truth. That there is only one absolute Truth
which is beyond all belief systems and only able to b
experienced first hand. Everything else, beyond th
direct experience of Truth now, can only ever be
relatively true belief existing in the conditioned min

Truth is always true

Remember, beliefs are only sometimes correct, in some circumstances, for a select few, in limited locations, at certain times. Absolute Truth, on the other hand, is always true, in all circumstances, for everyone, in all time and space. Any belief you have may appear correct to you, but I can guarantee someone else on the planet believes the exact opposite. This is why people can argue over beliefs, but never over the experience of truth. There is only one truth. Truth has no opposite. It is absolute. And therefore, Truth does not have sides to argue from.

Because beliefs are only relatively true, they aren't necessarily worth arguing over. What matters more is you experiencing Truth.

A reminder to remember

People fight over conflicting beliefs, but never argue over the experience of absolute truth. So notice if you are ever trying to be right. It is a sure sign that you've temporarily left the peace of the Real Self and you are in your mind thinking. The Truth is there is only Love. There is only this moment. There is only stillness. God doesn't make mistakes and nothing is ever wrong. But, hey, that's *my* Truth. You are free to believe whatever you want.

The peaceful solution

Let go of needing people to agree with your opinions by *experiencing* Truth yourself.

REASON #2
Being liked

Be warned. It is a very risky strategy to let you
peace be dependent upon whether people happen t
like you, or not. You have very little control ove
other people's opinions. And, unless the people i
your life are aware of their own Real Self, they ar
going to base *your* likeability on *their* unclear min
conditioning. They are not going to see you clearl
but rather, only see their vastly edited, drasticall
distorted ideas about you – based upon their ow
prejudices and judgements.

Give yourself permission to relax. Let other people
have whatever opinion they want. Focus on being
present, peaceful, and loving.

Being peacefully loving is the key that frees you fror
needing people to like you. It is so importan
because I've observed 'living out of love' (i.e
unaware of the Source of Love within you), as bein
one of the main causes of physical condition:
emotional unease and life stresses.

Based upon hundreds of Mind Detox consultation:
I've observed one core issue that sits at the heart o
most people's problems. Namely, the belief, an
subsequent distorted perception, that they ar
separate from the Source of Love. And therefor
have to *do* something to *be* lovable. Or, more crudel

tated: 'get' love. This belief makes them look for love outside of themselves and end up disappointed. Not because other people don't necessarily love them, but because the *outside love* is never as intimate or fulfilling as the love found within their own heart.

A reminder to remember

Tremendous peace of mind is experienced when resting in the inner still silent Source of Love. If you ever find yourself needing other people to like you, it means you've temporarily lost touch with your Real Self. The Truth is you don't need anyone to love you because You *are* Love. Play with this being a possibility. Notice what it's like to not look outside yourself for reassurance or respect. Be self-sufficient. Free yourself from fears about what people might think about you. Discover that you don't need the external world to love you for you to be OK.

The peaceful solution

Let go of needing people to like you by resting in the inner still silent Source of Love.

REASON #3
Problematic people

Anger, hurt and sadness are the common by-products of resisting the behaviours of others. For you to cultivate an on-going experience of peace then it is vital that you let go of making other people behave how you *think* they should. Or at the very least, make your peace more important than them changing their ways. Otherwise your peace is going to be victim to the uncontrollable actions of others.

Peaceful people don't pin their hopes for peace on the actions of others. In his book called Awareness Anthony De Mello said, *"we are not here to change the world, we are here to love it"*. I love the power of this simple truth. In only a few words he take the focus away from us trying to change the external world and places the power and responsibility in our own laps; specifically, in our willingness to learn how to love fully. I would also suggest we are not here to change other people, or make them behave how we *believe* they should. Rather, it is more useful to focus on learning how to love them as they are.

By love, I don't mean romantic love. Neither do mean you have to agree with their actions. Love is unconditional, non-judgmental and allows people to walk their own path to peace.

A reminder to remember
If you ever have a problem with how a person is behaving, play with not letting their actions impact your peace. Compassion is a great way of doing this. A compassionate person knows there are no bad people and everyone is doing their best to experience peace of mind, love and happiness. If someone is acting in a way you don't agree with then remember

they, like you, are doing their best. They don't know any better way, yet. Otherwise they would choose it. They need your compassion, not criticism.

The peaceful solution
Let go of people needing to behave how you *think* they should. Compassion sets you free.

REASON #4
Being on time

Within the context of you experiencing your hearts greatest desire of peace of mind, being on time may seem like a very unimportant reason over which to demote your peace. However it is one of the most common reasons that people get stressed and forget to be peaceful.

A while back, I got caught in busy traffic on my way to deliver a talk on 'Enjoying Peace of Mind'. Although the traffic had stopped, the clock continued to tick and I was quickly becoming late for my appointment. My mind automatically went into the future, started worrying about being late, and a tension appeared within my body.

After a minute or so I suddenly became aware of the stress that was forming over being late. I couldn't help but laugh out loud at how ironic it was that I was becoming stressed over arriving on time to a talk on Peace of Mind! It became blaringly obvious sitting in my car that day that I was going to get to my appointment as soon as I could. Getting stressed wasn't going to get me there any quicker. And it was a chance to prioritize peace and enjoy the journey.

Incidentally, as 'luck' would have it, when eventually did arrive at the venue for my talk, the fire alarm was ringing and everyone was waiting outside not for me, but for the fire brigade. Although I was officially late, I was actually early!

The peaceful solution
Let go of needing to be anywhere faster than the time you arrive.

REASON #5
Fixed future plans

Focusing too much on the future is a very quick way to misplace your present peace. Having fixed future plans can also limit your life enjoyment. Fixed plans can cause you to become controlling and resist life if it doesn't happen how you think it should.

However, what it is important to remember is that the future has a way of never working out *exactly* how you thought it would. Even if it does, it rarely manifests in the exact way you anticipated. So play with letting go of trying to make your life happen in any kind of way. Much freedom comes from making your inner experience of life more important than your external life circumstances. That way you don't mistakenly wait until your life is exactly how you think it should be before you get to enjoy it.

A reminder to remember

Attachment to future plans happens when you need the future to make you happy, peaceful and loved. However, as you already know, all of these wonderful treasures can only be experienced right now. So if you ever notice your peace and happiness becoming dependent upon things changing, improving, or becoming better at some point in the future, then stop.

Make your inner subjective experience of life more important than your objective life circumstances. Fill your attention up with *this* moment. Make the most of *this* moment. And let *this* moment be enough. You will find your attachment to future plans effortlessly falls away to be replaced with peace. You will discover when you are fully present that you don't need the future to fulfil you. You are already full and complete as you are. Everything beyond this moment is merely a potential bonus.

The peaceful solution

Let go of needing your life to happen how you *think* it should. Let this moment be enough.

THE ETERNAL GAME
Prioritizing your peace

For the next five days play with a peaceful solutio
each day and notice what happens to.

Day 1: Let go of needing people to agree with you
opinions by *experiencing* Truth yourself.
Day 2: Let go of needing people to like you by restin
in the inner still silent Source of Love.
Day 3: Let go of people needing to behave how yo
think they should.
Day 4: Let go of needing to be anywhere faster tha
the time you arrive.
Day 5: Let go of needing life to happen how yo
think it should. Let this moment be enough.

Then on Day 6 consider this: *What other things do
make more important than my peace?* For the next tw
days, play with making your peace more importar
than the items on your above list.

The eternal homework

Actually, this is going to be your homework foreve
or at least until we meet. Meditate every da
cultivate the habit of being aware of the still siler
peaceful context of *this* moment. There is no end
the levels of peace, love and happiness you ca
experience. The positive possibilities are endless!

IN CLOSING
Living in Love

Everything exists within a constant context of peace. By bringing your attention back to the still silent presence that exists within your awareness, always now, you immediately rest in the unbounded beauty and pristine peace of your Real Self. It becomes clear the presence you are experiencing *is* Love, unbounded, undiluted, unconditional Love. And that when you are resting fully aware of still silence you are Free.

Beyond the mind, you are beyond beliefs, beyond limitations, beyond judgments, beyond separation, beyond problems and beyond the past or future. You are present, peaceful and perfect right now.

Living in the real world

When preferences and goals rise up, you effortlessly and in a state of complete contentment, do whatever is required to make positive changes to your body or life. But because you are *already* perfectly peaceful, you are not attached to getting your preferences met or goals achieved. You are complete. Holding nothing you enjoy everything. You are surrendered to a wisdom that exists outside the parameters of your individual mind. Your attention is filled with love as you flow in the river of grace.

Experiencing the world with awe-filled eyes, you welcome life, however it may look and no longer resist life if it doesn't turn out exactly how you *think* it should. You experience no circumstances as wrong or emotions as negative.

Resistance and therefore unhealthy stress is no longer chronic or perpetual. Healing organically occurs, happiness naturally flows and peace is for life.

But the best news of all is *you can do it*. Peace is far easier than stress, resistance, pain and struggle. Give yourself permission to be at peace with your past by seeing beyond any misinformed beliefs. Rest in your Real Self by noticing the presence of still silent peace within your awareness now and play with taking life a little less seriously every day. You are walking the Path of Joy after all.

A marvelous way to live

To *Live in Love* is to directly experience the Source of Love within you. It is the master key that opens the door of health, abundance, of joy and of peace in your life, and in the wider world. It is a marvelous way to live. You experience your Real Self as a Love that is eternally present and absolutely infinite.

Sandy Newbigging

APPENDIX ONE

5-Step Method
At a glance

The 5-Step Method: *At a glance*

PART 1: DISCOVER the Unhealthy Beliefs

1. Find Root-Cause Event (WHEN it started?)
ASK: What event in my life is the cause of the problem, th
first event which when resolved will cause the problem t
disappear? If I were to know, what age was I?

2. Clarify the Context (WHAT happened?)
ASK: When I think of that time, what's the first person
place, event or thing to come to mind?
Digging deeper questions: Who was there?   Where was I
What was happening?

3. Discover Root-Cause Reason (WHY a problem?)
3.1 For emotion ASK: What is it about what happened tha
was a problem for me?   How did it make me feel?
3.2 For reason ASK: Ultimately, what was it about wha
happened that caused me to feel that way?
3.3 Rate Root-Cause Reason ASK: On a scale of 0 to 1(
with 10 being very high and feels true, how would I rat
(state Root-Cause Reason)?

PART 2: HEAL the Unhealthy Beliefs

4. Come to New Conclusions with New Info
(WHY NOT a problem now?)

4.1 Learn from past - ASK: What can I know now, that if I had known it in the past, I would have never felt (state Root-Cause Reason) in the first place?

4.2 Learn from future - ASK: Is it possible that I can be at peace when I think about this old event at some point in my life? If yes, when? OK, what will I know at that point in the future that will enable me to feel at peace then?

4.3 Learn from blind spot - ASK: For this to have been a problem, what did I need to not know?

Digging deeper question: For it to be a problem then, what did I need to believe? (Helps finds conclusion)

Use *Install the Knowing Exercise* when you discover a **positive** and **loving** learning that makes it impossible for you to have negative emotions associated with the RCE or RCR.

PART 3: <u>TEST</u> the Work

5. Test RCR is Resolved (Acknowledge Emotional Domino Benefits)

5.1 Test RCR: *On a scale of 10 to 0, with 0 being the emotion is completely gone now and I feel neutral, how do I rate the old Root-Cause Reason?*

5.2 Test the past: *On a scale of 10 to 0, with 0 being the emotion is completely gone now and I feel neutral, how would I rate the Root-Cause Event?*

5.3 Test the future: *Think of a time in the future when something like this could happen, but this time, notice how differently I respond, OK?*

APPENDIX TWO

The Top 20 Unhealthy Beliefs

(With associated Root-Cause Reasons)

Irrespective of what the physical, emotional or life problem is, during literally hundreds of Mind Detox consultations I've observed the same Unhealthy Beliefs appearing time and time again.

The top 20 most common Unhealthy Beliefs are shared in the following pages. Making sure you don't believe any of them can help you to heal current problems and prevent the on-set of future ones.

The claim

How can I make the claim that these Unhealth
Beliefs have the potential of causing physic
conditions? Here's how:

1. *When I met clients at my clinics, workshops*
residential retreats they had a physical condition,

2. *After the consultation(s) many clients reported the*
physical conditions getting better,

3. *The* **only** *thing we did during the consultation(s) w*
help them get peace with their past by discovering ar
healing their hidden Unhealthy Beliefs and associat
Root-Cause Reasons.

How to use the list

Unhealthy Beliefs have Root-Cause Reasons (RCI
that provide mental and emotional evidence th
justifies them being true (for you). If you find a
Unhealthy Belief in the Top-20 list that feels true, yo
then want to find the corresponding RCR(s) that a
justifying the belief.

ollow these steps:

Read the list of Unhealthy Beliefs and notice hether any of them feel true to you and/or if you ave evidence that proves their validity.

Once you discover an Unhealthy Belief that sonates with you, turn to the subsequent pages to nd real-life examples of Root-Cause Reasons (RCR) at I've found to be justifying the Unhealthy Belief.

Read through the list to find the RCR that most sonates with you. Place a tick in the box beside it. ou may notice reading others that your own RCR mes to mind that better fits your personal xperience. Write it down if it does.

Once you've discovered the Unhealthy Belief and rresponding RCR, then do your best to remember a roblematic event from the past that is linked with e RCR. For instance, if your RCR is "sad I'm bad", en think of a memory in the past when you felt sad cause you thought you'd been bad. Having a emory is useful when it comes to healing the belief.

Once you have the Unhealthy Belief, RCR and emory, go to Chapter 6: Heal your Unhealthy eliefs, so you can achieve peace with your past.

Reality is what is real right now...

All you are exploring and changing here is you imagination. You are not time travelling and you past is no longer happening. Right now, you are saf and you will remain so throughout. These Unhealth Beliefs may feel true but they are not absolutely true.

Remembering this can help the entire process b comfortable and even enjoyable! If you are in an doubt about your ability to go through this proces on your own please consult a qualified Mind Deto Practitioner (by using the Practitioner Finder a www.minddetox.com).

THE LIST
Top 20 Unhealthy Beliefs

1. *"My parents didn't love me enough"*
2. *"I'm unloved"*
3. *"I'm unwanted"*
4. *"I'm rejected"*
5. *"I'm on my own"*
6. *"I'm abandoned"*
7. *"Someone important left me"*
8. *"There's nobody there for me"*
9. *"I'm alone, lonely and/or isolated"*
10. *"There is something wrong with me"*
11. *"I'm bad"*
12. *"I'm not good enough"*
13. *"I've let others down"*
14. *"I'm let down by others"*
15. *"It should not have happened that way"*
16. *"I've lost someone/something I love"*
17. *"I feel bad for others"*
18. *"I'm not able to do what I want"*
19. *"I'm unprotected, unsafe, and/or vulnerable"*
20. *"I can't stop bad things happening"*

Other common Unhealthy Beliefs include:

There's something wrong"
"I'm weak"
"I'm confused"
"It's my fault"
"I'm separate from the Source of Love"

Real-life Root-Cause Reasons justifying the most common Unhealthy Beliefs

IMPORTANT: It is **NOT** recommended that you read through all of the following Root-Cause Reasons because they do not necessarily make for light reading! Just read the examples listed below the Unhealthy Belief(s) that feel most true to you.

1. Real-life Root-Cause Reasons justifying the belief _"My parents did not love me enough"_ include:

☐ _"Sad not loved by mum and dad"_
☐ _"Hurt that dad loves mum more than me"_
☐ _"Sad mum & dad didn't care enough"_
☐ _"Sad, scared & vulnerable my parents didn't care about me"_
☐ _"Sad and vulnerable dad didn't love me"_
☐ _"Hurt, sad & rejected mum and dad loved my brother more"_
☐ _"Sad, hurt & abandoned not cared about"_
☐ _"Sad dad doesn't love me"_
☐ _"Sad mum & dad couldn't be arsed helping me"_
☐ _"Hurt, sad & scared mum didn't want me"_
☐ _"Sad, scared & vulnerable dad didn't fight for me"_
☐ _"Sad, alone & left out parents didn't love me as much"_
☐ _"Hurt, sad & vulnerable mum didn't love me"_
☐ _"Sad my parents preferred my brother"_
☐ _"Sad I don't feel loved & supported by mum and dad"_
☐ _"Hurt that my mum & dad resent me"_
☐ _"Angry & sad mum & dad didn't give a shit about me"_
☐ _"Sad dad doesn't love me for who I am"_
☐ _"Hurt mum didn't tell me she loved me"_

2. Real-life Root-Cause Reasons justifying the belief: *"I'm unloved"* include:

- [ ] *"Left out & lonely not loved as much"*
- [ ] *"Hurt & angry not cared about"*
- [ ] *"Sad & alone not loved"*
- [ ] *"Sad I don't matter"*
- [ ] *"Alone & lonely because I'm not loveable"*
- [ ] *"Scared of not being loved"*
- [ ] *"Sad I don't know why I'm not liked"*
- [ ] *"Sad & scared not liked"*
- [ ] *"Sad, scared & vulnerable not loved by mum"*
- [ ] *"I need to work hard in order to be loved"*
- [ ] *"Sad & useless not loveable as I am"*
- [ ] *"Hurt, sad & scared not loveable"*

3. Real-life Root-Cause Reasons justifying the belief: *"I'm unwanted"* include:

- [ ] *"Sad treated so unfairly all the time because I'm not wanted"*
- [ ] *"Hurt & worthless not loved & accepted for who I am"*
- [ ] *"Hurt mum & dad didn't accept me"*
- [ ] *"Sad that I'm not wanted"*
- [ ] *"Scared I'm not needed"*
- [ ] *"Empty because I don't matter"*
- [ ] *"Sad, vulnerable & scared that nobody wants me"*
- [ ] *"Lonely & isolated never good enough to have a best friend"*
- [ ] *"Hurt that I'm not noticed"*
- [ ] *"Feel worthless & not wanted"*
- [ ] *"Sad & angry that I don't matter"*
- [ ] *"Sad & worthless when people are happy without me"*

☐ *"Scared & alone because I'm not wanted"*
☐ *"Sad unwanted because I was a girl"*
☐ *"Hurt there's something wrong with me & I'm not wanted"*
☐ *"Sad dad didn't want me"*
☐ *"Sad parents didn't want me"*
☐ *"Hurt, sad & vulnerable mum & dad sent me away"*

4. Real-life Root-Cause Reasons justifying the belief *"I'm rejected"* include:

☐ *"Hurt & rejected by people"*
☐ *"Hurt, rejected & worthless mum doesn't love me"*
☐ *"Scared of being hurt & rejected by someone I love"*
☐ *"Sad, angry & worthless I was rejected & replaced"*
☐ *"Hurt & rejected because I was a girl"*
☐ *"Sad & rejected when misunderstood"*
☐ *"Sad my brother rejected me"*
☐ *"Sad rejected by mum"*
☐ *"Sad, hurt, unwanted & rejected when people leave me"*
☐ *"Hurt rejected by my dad"*

5. Real-life Root-Cause Reasons justifying the belief *"I'm on my own"* include:

☐ *"Left out & alone"*
☐ *"Sad, scared & vulnerable on my own"*
☐ *"Scared when I'm on my own"*
☐ *"Lost, alone & lonely on my own"*
☐ *"Sad they are going to leave me on my own"*

] *"Scared & alone left on my own"*
] *"Isolated & vulnerable I'm on my own"*
] *"Helpless completely on my own"*
] *"Sad about being left out"*
] *"Sad, sick & lonely when I'm left to survive on my own"*
] *"Let down, lost & lonely left to get by on my own"*
] *"Sad, lonely, left alone & having to do things on my own"*

. Real-life Root-Cause Reasons justifying the belief: *I'm abandoned"* include:

] *"Scared of being abandoned"*
] *"Sad everyone I love abandons me"*
] *"Sad & scared abandoned by my mum"*
] *"Hurt & angry that I was abandoned"*
] *"Abandoned in my moment of need"*
] *"Completely lost & abandoned not cared about"*
] *"Sad, lonely & helpless when abandoned & left behind"*
] *"Alone & abandoned not cared about"*
] *"Sad, shocked & confused abandoned by mum"*
] *"Hurt, sad & scared not safe abandoned by mum"*
] *"Terrified abandoned by mum"*

. Real-life Root-Cause Reasons justifying the belief: *Someone important left me"* include:

] *"Hurt, scared & alone when mum left"*
] *"Sad dad left me behind"*
] *"Sad, scared, alone & vulnerable when dad left me"*

☐ *"Hurt & angry mum & dad left us"*
☐ *"Scared & hopeless when people I love leave"*
☐ *"Sad I miss the people I love"*
☐ *"Sad, scared & vulnerable parents left me on my own"*
☐ *"Sad, hurt & unwanted when people leave me"*

8. Real-life Root-Cause Reasons justifying the belie
"There's nobody there for me" include:

☐ *"Sad nobody there for me"*
☐ *"Sad dad wasn't there for me"*
☐ *"Sad, weak & rejected nobody there for me"*
☐ *"Sad & alone without my soul mate there for me"*
☐ *"Lost & alone nobody there for me"*
☐ *"Sad & lonely nobody there for me"*
☐ *"Sad, scared & vulnerable not looked after"*
☐ *"Sad, scared & vulnerable nobody there for me"*
☐ *"Sad, scared & alone nobody there for me"*
☐ *"Sad nobody there to help me"*
☐ *"Sad, lonely & isolated mum & dad not there for me"*

9. Real-life Root-Cause Reasons justifying the belie
"I'm alone, lonely and/or isolated" include:

☐ *"Sad I'm so isolated"*
☐ *"Sad nobody to play with"*
☐ *"Lonely & isolated with no support"*
☐ *"Sad that I'm alone in the universe"*
☐ *"Sad & lonely my sister didn't want to be seen with me"*
☐ *"Sick, scared & vulnerable when left out & not liked"*

☐ *"Sad & lonely not seen or understood"*
☐ *"Sad & isolated when unfairly ganged up upon"*
☐ *"Sad & helpless when people turn & walk away"*
☐ *"Left out & alone nobody to turn to"*
☐ *"Sad, lost & lonely nobody there for me"*
☐ *"Sad I had nobody"*
☐ *"Sad & lonely because I'm alone & not liked"*
☐ *"Lonely & isolated coz mum & dad split up"*
☐ *"Sad, lost & alone dad's gone"*
☐ *"Sad & vulnerable dad's gone"*
☐ *"Lonely & isolated because I should be something else"*
☐ *"Sad dad not there to comfort me"*
☐ *"Sad & scared people think I'm disgusting & exclude me"*
☐ *"Sad & angry when separated from mum"*
☐ *"Scared of being alone & lonely"*
☐ *"Sad, scared & isolated because I'm fat"*

0. Real-life Root-Cause Reasons justifying the belief: **"There's something wrong with me"** include:

☐ *"Guilty because I should have been a boy"*
☐ *"Hurt, sad & angry always told something wrong with me"*
☐ *"Sad, scared & guilty there's something wrong with me"*
☐ *"Sad & frustrated always something wrong with me"*
☐ *"Scared of being exposed as a fraud"*
☐ *"Sad there's something wrong with me"*
☐ *"Hurt, angry & guilty made to feel dirty"*
☐ *"Shame from being violated & dirty"*
☐ *"Sad, scared & vulnerable when I do something wrong"*
☐ *"Upset that I felt stupid"*
☐ *"Angry made to look stupid"*

☐ *"Sad, alone & not loveable because I'm different"*
☐ *"Sad & lonely I'm different"*

11. Real-life Root-Cause Reasons justifying the belief: *"I'm bad"* include:

☐ *"Sad I'm bad"*
☐ *"Sad not normal"*
☐ *"Sad I'm ugly"*
☐ *"Sad & guilty I'm naughty"*
☐ *"Sad I don't deserve to be alive"*
☐ *"Sad & shame because I'm stupid"*
☐ *"Hurt, sad & guilty that I'm bad"*
☐ *"Hurt, isolated & alone there's something wrong with me"*
☐ *"I'm worthless compared to others"*
☐ *"Sad I'm a bad person"*
☐ *"Hurt, sad & worthless I'm not doing it right"*

12. Real-life Root-Cause Reasons justifying the belief *"I'm not good enough"* include:

☐ *"Sad never good enough for dad"*
☐ *"Hurt about not being good enough"*
☐ *"Deflated that my best is never good enough"*
☐ *"I'm not good enough to meet my soul mate"*
☐ *"Sad not good enough for other people to want to be with me"*
☐ *"Sad never good enough for the people I love"*
☐ *"I'm shit & worthless compared to others"*
☐ *"Sad I'm always second best"*

] *"Sad & isolated because I'm not important"*
] *"Hurt always wrong & never good enough for mum"*
] *"Sad & rejected because I'm not good enough"*

3. Real-life Root-Cause Reasons justifying the belief: *I've let others down"* include:

] *"Sad let dad down"*
] *"Sad & guilty that dad has never been proud of me"*
] *"Sad let my mum down"*
] *"Sad & guilty I disappointed my dad"*
] *"Panic about letting dad down"*
] *"Sad & guilty that I've failed & let my parents down"*
] *"Sad that I've let my parents down"*
] *"Feel really bad that I've hurt my mum"*
] *"Sad & guilty not there for my mum"*
] *"Sad I couldn't help mum"*
] *"Sad & guilty I couldn't save my parents"*
] *"Sad that I've not been there for my mum"*
] *"Scared to let people down"*

4. Real-life Root-Cause Reasons justifying the belief: *I'm let down by others"* include:

] *"Sad let down by the people I love"*
] *"Scared of being hurt by people close to me"*
] *"Lost, alone & let down by partner"*
] *"Hurt about being let down"*
] *"Sad & lonely nobody understood me"*
] *"Hurt mum always put herself first"*

- ☐ *"Hurt, angry & disgusted at dad"*
- ☐ *"Let down that dad was so selfish"*
- ☐ *"Scared dad wasn't in control"*
- ☐ *"Sad dad never supported me"*
- ☐ *"Hurt & sad that dad was mean to me"*
- ☐ *"Angry dad bullied the confidence out of me"*
- ☐ *"Hate dad dominating me"*
- ☐ *"Hurt let down by dad"*
- ☐ *"Pissed-off because I hate dads wife"*
- ☐ *"Angry I never got support"*
- ☐ *"Sad & scared dad left me alone with mum"*
- ☐ *"Hurt, stupid & worthless when brother put me down"*
- ☐ *"Sad, scared & alone when betrayed by partner"*
- ☐ *"Angry people do things I don't want them to do"*

REMEMBER: You are a good person. You always do your best. Your intentions are positive. And nothing can ever impact your lovability. You *are* Love!

15. Real-life Root-Cause Reasons justifying the belief: *"It should not have happened that way"* include:

- ☐ *"Sad I didn't get to know my mum"*
- ☐ *"Sad I've wasted my life"*
- ☐ *"Sad my kids don't have grandparents"*
- ☐ *"Sad I got rid of my first baby"*
- ☐ *"Shame & guilt that I let X abuse me for so long"*
- ☐ *"Sad, lost & alone falling apart after abortion"*
- ☐ *"Sad dad died before I got to know him"*
- ☐ *"Sad that I shouldn't have been born"*

❏ *"Sad I wasn't close to my parents"*
❏ *"Sad missed out on attention from my mum"*
❏ *"Sad he couldn't come to me for help"*
❏ *"Angry because I was forced to do things I didn't want to do"*
❏ *"Sad & guilty I was too busy & missed time with my child"*

16. Real-life Root-Cause Reasons justifying the belief: *"I've lost someone/something I love"* include:

❏ *"Sad I lost my dad"*
❏ *"Sad & overwhelmed I've lost the people I love"*
❏ *"Sad, scared & alone when I lose the people I love"*
❏ *"Hurt, sad & scared that people I love leave me"*
❏ *"Sad I lost my brother"*
❏ *"Empty when I lose the people I love"*
❏ *"Sad, left out & lonely when people I love are taken away"*
❏ *"Sad & scared of losing people I love"*
❏ *"Sad to lose people I love"*
❏ *"Sad & scared everything was breaking down"*
❏ *"Sad & scared about losing dads love"*
❏ *"Hurt coz the people I love don't love me enough to stay"*
❏ *"Sad I lost my child & missed out on having a family"*

17. Real-life Root-Cause Reasons justifying the belief: *"I feel bad for others"* include:

❏ *"Sad my dad was so weak & vulnerable'*
❏ *"Sad & scared dad was so pathetic"*
❏ *"Sad my dad is sad"*
❏ *"Sad & scared to see dad hurt & vulnerable"*

- ☐ *"Tired of carrying my dads heaviness"*
- ☐ *"Sad & scared to see mum so weak"*
- ☐ *"Sad & guilty to see my mum hurting"*
- ☐ *"Sad & alone mum gets upset & can't help me"*
- ☐ *"Sad & weak not able to help my mum"*
- ☐ *"Sad & scared to see dad so ill & weak"*
- ☐ *"Scared of mum being upset"*
- ☐ *"Angry mums parents hurt my mum"*
- ☐ *"Sad & helpless to see my dad suffering"*
- ☐ *"Sad & scared mum so vulnerable"*

18. Real-life Root-Cause Reasons justifying the belief *"I'm not able to do what I want"* include:

- ☐ *"Stuck & helpless not free to do what I want"*
- ☐ *"Hate being told what do to"*
- ☐ *"Angry not able to do what I want"*
- ☐ *"Sad & stuck not free to be me"*
- ☐ *"Pissed off at petty rules"*
- ☐ *"Sad they don't care about what I want"*
- ☐ *"Hurt not allowed to do what I want to do"*
- ☐ *"Helpless I can't do anything to fix it"*
- ☐ *"Scared & powerless not able to stop bad things happening"*
- ☐ *"Sad & angry not able to complete my life purpose"*
- ☐ *"I'm frustrated that I'm not able to do what I want"*

REMEMBER: If you want to see something inspirational, then look in a mirror! You have already accomplished so much with your life. You are more confident than you think. You can do it!

9. Real-life Root-Cause Reasons justifying the belief: *I'm unprotected, unsafe, weak or vulnerable"* include:

] *"Sad & vulnerable mum didn't protect me"*
] *"Lonely & vulnerable dad not there"*
] *"Let down & vulnerable brother didn't protect me"*
] *"Scared, vulnerable & unprotected'*
] *"Sad I was violated"*
] *"Scared that people will see that I'm vulnerable"*
] *"Scared & helpless I couldn't stop them hurting me"*
] *"Scared of being exposed"*
] *"Scared & alone struggling for life"*
] *"Scared & vulnerable dad's so unpredictable"*
] *"Hurt, scared & helpless couldn't tell him to stop"*
] *"Scared & vulnerable when out of control"*
] *"Scared & weak when people see I'm weak"*
] *"Scared left alone with nobody to protect me"*
] *"Hurt, unprotected & violated"*
] *"Sad & scared helpless & vulnerable"*
] *"Hurt & isolated not safe"*
] *"Sad I couldn't stop my dad from hurting me"*
] *"Scared of being weak"*
] *"Sad & alone nobody there to stick up for me"*
] *"Scared to be weak & crumble"*
] *"Scared of being hurt when exposed & open"*
] *"Vulnerable when I'm outside my home"*
] *"Scared of people seeing me"*
] *"Scared & vulnerable of dad hurting me"*
] *"Scared my life is so vulnerable"*
] *"Tired of feeling suffocated & powerless"*
] *"Vulnerable when people invade my space"*

☐ *"Sad & frightened not protected by dad"*
☐ *"Scared, alone & vulnerable nobody there to protect me"*

20. Real-life Root-Cause Reasons justifying the belie *"I can't stop bad things happening"* include:

☐ *"Scared of being hurt"*
☐ *"Sad & scared of getting things wrong"*
☐ *"Scared to be homeless"*
☐ *"Scared I'm going to die"*
☐ *"Sad & scared to lose my safety net"*
☐ *"Scared of being stuck"*
☐ *"Scared something bad is going to happen"*
☐ *"Scared people I love could get hurt"*
☐ *"Sad & scared of being abused"*
☐ *"Scared of hurting my kids in the same way I was hurt"*
☐ *"Scared to get it wrong & hurt the people I love"*
☐ *"Scared of mum & dad splitting up"*
☐ *"Petrified of getting ill like my mother"*
☐ *"Scared of losing what I've got"*
☐ *"Scared of losing my mum & dad"*
☐ *"Scared that I will end up like mum"*
☐ *"Scared I can't cope"*
☐ *"Scared of screwing up"*
☐ *"Sad & scared that I'm going to get into trouble"*

REMEMBER: Holding grudges hurts the hands tha hold them. You do not have to agree with the actior of others to heal your relationship with the pas Compassion sets you free!

APPENDIX THREE

Extra tools for enjoying peace

TOOL #1
Results or Reasons

A good friend shared this tool with me at a time i
my life when I was feeling overwhelmed. It helpe
me to gain clarity on what I wanted and understan
what was preventing me from getting what I wante
in life. I hope it helps you too.

In life, you either get the results you want or th
reasons why you're not getting what you want.

RESULTS
There are two types of results a person can get:

1. States
Examples of states include being happy, peacefu
confident, loving, contented and so on.

2. Outcomes
Examples of outcomes include getting a job, meetin
someone, going on holiday etc.

REASONS
If you are currently not enjoying the results you war
in life, then there are three reasons why you're no
getting what they want:

1. Negative Emotions
Examples of negative emotions include - ange
sadness, fear, guilt, hurt, grief and anxiety.

Unhealthy Beliefs

Unhealthy Beliefs usually start with *"I can't... I'll never... I'm not... I'm the sort of person who..."* etc. As you know from this book, your Unhealthy Beliefs can impact your body, your emotions, your behaviours and your life.

Ineffective Behaviours (Strategies)

The way you are trying to get the results you want is ineffective. For instance, spending more money than you earn (long term) may be an ineffective strategy for becoming financially free. Or eating sugar-filled toxic 'food' is an ineffective way of being slim and healthy.

KEEPING LIFE SIMPLE

You either get results or reasons so by using the methods shared within this book you can clear the reasons so you automatically get more of the results you want. Use this table to gain clarity:

RESULTS What states and outcomes do I want?	REASONS What emotions, beliefs or behaviours stop me?

TOOL #2
My Incorrect Conclusions

Remember, Unhealthy Beliefs are incorrec
conclusions that you've come to at some point i
your past. This exercise helps you discover unhealthy
conclusions that you may not have been aware o
even believing.

PART 1: **STARTER SENTENCES**

Without editing your thoughts, finish the followin
sentences with the first words that come to mind
Aim to get a few answers for each starter sentence:

I'm...
I'm not...
I always get...
I always feel...
I'm too...
I will never...
It's hard to...
I'm the sort of person who...

PART 2: **LIFE AREAS**

Now hold the following life areas in your mind an
notice the first thoughts you have. For instance, fo
money, you might have a thought *'it's hard to mak
money'* or *'I will never get out of debt"*. Or, fo
Love/Intimacy, you might think *'I will never meet m*

soul mate' or whatever. Notice the first thoughts that come to mind when you think about the following areas and note them in a journal:

Family / Friends
Love / Intimacy
Career / Work
Money
Spirituality

NEXT STEPS

Found any unhelpful conclusions? Turn to Part 2 of this book to take positive steps to heal them. You can do this by using the 5-Step method to discover the root-cause event when you first came to the unhelpful conclusion.

Alternatively, you can get started on healing the unhelpful conclusion immediately by turning the page to use the Decision Destroyer Tool.

TOOL #3
Decision Destroyer

Imagine you catch yourself (or a friend) saying ar Unhealthy Belief like, *'People I love leave'* or *'It's hard to make money'* or *'I can't lose weight'* or whatever. There are a couple questions you can ask to challenge the Unhealthy Belief and, in some cases, completely hea it in seconds.

The interesting thing about beliefs is that there is often a moment prior to forming the belief when you either consciously or unconsciously made a decision So this means many Unhealthy Beliefs are preceded by an unhealthy decision. This exercise can help you to go back in time (in your mind), make a more positive decision, and as a result, form of more healthy belief.

INSTRUCTIONS
Temporarily hold the unhelpful belief in your mind whilst trusting your first answer to this question:

"When did I decide that?"

You may get a number pop into your mind and/or a memory. Amazingly, most people I ask this question to immediately remember the exact moment they formed the Unhealthy Belief. Once you have a possible memory, ask:

216

"What was I deciding before that?"

Keep asking the second question (going earlier and earlier in time) until you find a decision that is purely positive and loving. It may feel like you are making it up and there is no way of knowing what you were actually thinking then. That is completely normal. The purpose of this exercise is to track back in your mind until you come across a more positive decision. (Which is probably going to be the opposite of the unhelpful belief!) Then take a deep breath and come back to now, bringing the positive decision with you. Trust your unconscious mind to do this for you. You may now find the old Unhealthy Belief feels less true if you think about it.

TOP TIP:
Family friendly

This is a great tool that can be used very casually with your kids over the kitchen table or with a friend over a cup of tea. Give it a go and have fun!

TOOL #4
Emotional Freedom Technique

A simple, yet effective method for clearing blocke
emotions, Emotional Freedom Technique (EFT), ha
been described as physiological acupuncture.
involves tapping certain points of the body, whic
correspond with acupuncture points, while sayir
short phrases relating to the problem you wish
release and resolve.

EFT has proven successful in thousands of clinic
cases and I have used it many times to help people
comfortably and quickly let go of all forms
negative emotions, change Unhealthy Beliefs ar
even cure health conditions. I've included the EF
instructions so you can give it a go on the mo
stubborn emotionally fuelled Root-Cause Reasons.

Using EFT with my 5-Step Method

Use EFT to release the emotions associated with th
Root-Cause Reason statements you discover usir
my Method. This can help to release them from th
cellular memory of the body-mind and proves ve
effective for getting peace with your past.

INSTRUCTIONS
Once you've clarified the Root-Cause Reason (usir
Steps 1-3 of my Method), follow these steps:

STEP #1: **The set-up statement**

Repeat the set-up statement three times while tapping the Karate Chop (KC) point located on the side of the hand (see Diagram 1): *'Even though I (state Root-Cause Reason), I love and accept myself.'* For example: *'Even though I'm sad my dad left, I love and accept myself.'*

STEP #2: **The round of tapping**

Tap seven to nine times on each of the meridian points while repeating the Root-Cause Reason at each point (see Diagram 1 for location of meridian points):

Quick reminder:
TH, EB, SE, UE, UN, CH, CB, AP, L, TH, IF, MF, LF

STEP #3: **The 9 gamut procedure**

Continuously tap, rub or hold the gamut point (see Diagram 1) while performing this sequence: close your eyes – open your eyes – look hard down to the right – look hard down to the left – roll your eyes one way – roll your eyes in the other direction – hum two seconds of a song you love – count from five down to zero – hum two more seconds of a uplifting song.

STEP #4: **Repeat the round**

Tap about seven to nine times on each of the meridian points (TH to LF) again, but this time, feel free to say positive learning (see Chapter 6 for suggestions) on some of the points – this can help tap in' healthier conclusions.

STEP #5: **Re-rate the emotional intensity of problem**
Take a deep breath and measure the problem again
using the Step 5 questions from my method:

TEST THE PAST: *"On a scale of 10 to 0, with 0 being th*
emotion is completely gone now and you feel neutral, how
would I rate the Root-Cause Event?

TEST ROOT-CAUSE REASON: *"On a scale of 10 to 0*
with 0 being the emotion is completely gone now and you
feel neutral, how would I rate the old Root-Cause Reason?

TEST THE FUTURE *"Think of a time in the future when*
something like this could happen, but this time, notice how
differently I respond, OK?"

If it is higher than 0 then repeat the sequence from 1-
with the new set-up statement: *'Even though I still fee*
'sad dad left' I deeply and completely love and accept
appreciate and respect, honour and forgive myself.' The
on each point, say 'Remaining sadness about dad leaving
for example.

Remember, if after doing EFT the emotion stay
above 0 it means you have a blind spot justifying th
emotion so explore Chapter 6 and install the learnin
you need so you no longer feel justified to feel an
negative emotions associated with the RCE or RCR.

Diagram 1: EFT Points

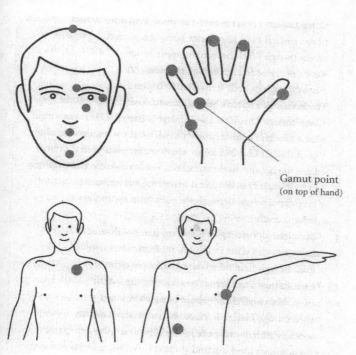

Gamut point
(on top of hand)

Key to the meridian points:

TH: top of head

EB: eyebrow,

SE: side of eye

UE: under eye

UN: under nose

CH: chin

CB: collarbone

AP: armpit

L: liver

TH: thumb

IF: index finger

MF: middle finger

LF: little finger

KC: karate chop

TOOL #5
3C Vision

3C Vision is a remarkable way to clear your mind
and feel calm, confident and content in any situation.

<u>INSTRUCTIONS:</u>

1 Pick a spot on a wall to look at, ideally above eye level (at
about a 45° angle), so that as you look at it, it feels as
though your vision is bumping up against your eyebrows.

2 As you stare at the spot on the wall, effortlessly let your
mind go loose and focus all of your attention on the spot.
At this point you may find yourself wanting to take a deep
breath in and out. Let yourself do so.

3 Notice that within a matter of a few moments, your
vision will begin to spread out. You will begin to see more
in the peripheral than in the central part of your vision.

4 Now, pay more attention to the peripheral part of your
vision than to the central part of your vision. Notice
colours, shadows, shapes and so on. Notice what you see
on the left and right, above and below (without looking
directly at anything to keep using peripheral vision).

5 Continue for as long as you want while noticing how it
feels. Notice if your mind has become more still.

With a little practice you will be able to use 3C Vision as
you go about your day – when reading, out walking,
chatting with people, pretty much anytime you want to
feel calm, confident and content.

TOOL #6
D.I.Y. Mind Detox

WHEN Find Age	*What event in my life is the cause of the problem, the first event that when resolved, will cause my problem to disappear?* *If I were to know, what age was I?*
WHAT Root-Cause Event	*When I think of that time, what's the first person, place, event or thing that comes to mind?*
WHY Root-Cause Reason	*How did what happened make me feel?* *Ultimately, what was it about what happened that caused me to feel that way?*
WHY NOT Loving Learning	*What can I know now, that if I had known it in the past, I would have never felt any negative emotions in the first place?*
NOW USE 'INSTALL THE KNOWING' EXERCISE	

Notes

Notes

Notes

Notes

Notes

NEXT STEPS
Your path of peace continues

You're going to love what you can do next...

CLUB: Join Sandy's online club where you can access videos, audios and articles and special offers.

CLINICS: Experience a private one-to-one consultation with Sandy or find a Mind Detox Practitioner near you using Sandy's online Practitioner Finder.

COURSES: Learn more advanced forms of meditation with Sandy that are only ever taught in person.

RETREATS: Experience Sandy's unique mind-body-soul approach to health, peace and happiness at one of his residential retreats. Highly recommended!

ACADEMY: Make a positive difference to the lives of others by training with Sandy to become a qualified Mind Detox Method (MDM) Practitioner.

For more info, visit: **www.sandynewbigging.com**

229

About the author

Sandy Newbigging is the creator of the Mind Detox Method, a meditation teacher, and author of Life Detox and Life-Changing Weight Loss. His work has been seen on television worldwide on channels including Discovery Health. He has clinics in the UK, runs residential retreats internationally, and trains Mind Detox Practitioners via his Academy.

peace for life

Freedom from problems for good

SANDY NEWBIGGING

Until next time… prioritise your peace!